Wonder Wise

AUTHOR/PROGRAM DESIGNER

Karen Cornelsen Heizer

ARTIST
Judith B. Fischer

POET
Diane Peck

Idea Factory, Inc.
10710 Dixon Drive
Riverview, Florida

WONDER WISE
Karen Cornelsen Heizer

IDEA FACTORY, INC.
10710 Dixon Drive
Riverview, FL 33569
1-800-331-6204
FAX (813) 677-0373

ISBN 1-885041-06-3

Printed and bound in the United States of America

Dedication

This book was written in gratitude and loving tribute to the brave crew of the United States of America space shuttle Challenger.

Wonder Wise has been made possible by a federally funded program honoring the late teacher in space, Christa McAuliffe.

A very special thanks to the United States Department of Education, The Oklahoma State Department of Education, Enid Public Schools, and the Wonder Wise teams.

A very special note of gratitude and thanks to friends, colleagues and members of my family – especially Bill, Miah, and Kendra your support, help, and encouragement are a most treasured gift.

To my parents Jerry and Mary Cornelsen, who taught me to be kind and work hard, and whose Christian beliefs, morals, and leadership inspired my life –

May you all know how vital you are to the pages of my life and happiness.

Meet The *Wonder Wise* Team

EXECUTIVE/ADVISORY BOARD

Karen Heizer, Teacher
Author/Presidential Awardee
Christa McAuliffe Fellow

Bob Lepischak, Teacher
. International Council of
Associations of Science
Education (ICASE)

Judith B. Fischer, Publications Director
Fischer Art & Design

Diane Peck, Poet
Enid, Oklahoma

Doris Grigsby, Science Specialist
National Aeronautics & Space Administration

Sandi Schlichting, President
Idea Factory, Inc.

Steve Marshall, Teacher
London, England

Russel Rapose, Curriculum Specialist
Rhode Island, United States

Beverley McMillan, Teacher
Presidential Awardee

Anna Stracner, Teacher
NASA Facilitator

Betsy Mabry, Teacher
Oklahoma Teacher of the Year

ASSESSMENT

Mary Sweet, Ph. D.
Educational Psychologist
Enid, Oklahoma

Dr. Jan McDonald, Ph. D.
Dean, School of
Mathematics Education
Enid, Oklahoma

Kay Kiner, M. Ed
Reading and Learning
Disabilities Specialist
Enid, Oklahoma

Steve Marshall
London, England

CURRICULUM/TEACHER CONSULTATION

Delores Brown
Enid, Oklahoma

Debbie Evans
Enid, Oklahoma

Elizabeth Morris
Enid, Oklahoma

Ann Redding
Enid, Oklahoma

Mary Sweet
Enid, Oklahoma

Tracy Bugg
Enid, Oklahoma

Betsy Mabry
Enid, Oklahoma

Shirley Peterson
Kansas City, Kansas

Janie Steele
Big Lake, Texas

Jan and Ty Voss
Enid, Oklahoma

Rhonda Craig
Enid, Oklahoma

Steve Marshall
London, England

Russell Rapose
Narragansett, Rhode Island

Anna Stracner
Burneyville, Oklahoma

EDITING

Delores Brown
Betsy Mabry
Diane Peck
Ann Redding
Anna Stracner

Judith Fischer
Steve Marshall
Shirley Peterson
Sandi Schlichting

WIZARD PEER TEACHING RESEARCH COACH

Shirley Peterson

LEGAL/COPYRIGHT ADVISORS

Litman Law Office
Arlington, Virginia

FINANCIAL/ACCOUNTING CONSULTATION

Pat Donehue, CPA
Enid, Oklahoma

Connie Ratliff, Accountant
Dumas, Texas

COMPUTER CONSULTATION

Sean Peck
Stillwater, Oklahoma

Pete Peterson
Enid, Oklahoma

FACILITATING TEAM

Delores Brown
Betsy Mabry
Sandi Schlichting

Karen Heizer
Beverly McMillan
Anna Stracner

ON–SITE TRAINING/RESEARCH

Glenwood Elementary, Enid Public Schools
Enid, Oklahoma
Dr. Kem Keithly, Superindentent

Table of Contents

Wonder Wise – A Rationale

Students enter school filled with curiosity about the world around them. They have a natural need to know "how" things work and "why" things happen. If science is presented as a body of factual knowledge to be delivered to the student by the teacher, students soon become overwhelmed trying to memorize numerous unrelated facts.

Wonder Wise is an integrated hands–on science program for young learners and a facilitating methodology for teachers. *Wonder Wise* provides the opportunity for students to have a multi–sensory, whole language experience **starting with science activities**. The activities are designed to follow a step–by–step learning cycle. The questioning techniques are "kid friendly" and encourage sharing and application of prior knowledge.

Traditionally teachers are required to teach so much of everything in a given day, that sometimes, nothing gets taught well. Students have become robotic learners as they open a textbook, read, and then answer the questions at the end of the chapter. When textbooks are put away students sometimes are able to recite memorized facts, while retention and application remain weak and meaningless. Students see little or no application of their school lesson to the real world. *Wonder Wise* addresses teaching the child, not just a factual concept. The *Wonder Wise* way starts with hands–on science activities, uses the textbook as a resource, and then expands, challenges, and integrates into related core subjects.

Wonder Wise uses science process skills and inquiry strategies to help students develop the habits of mind important to all curriculum areas. Science processes – observing, classifying, inferring, communicating, measuring, using numbers, predicting, interpreting data, hypothesizing, controlling variables, experimenting, formulating mental models, and defining operationally, are the core of science. Process skills are also the common thinking skills woven through all subject areas and learning experiences. *Wonder Wise* integrated activities provide excellent opportunities for developing and reinforcing thinking skills that students can carry to all their experiences, both in and out of school. Children develop conceptual understanding by processing information and experiences. The development of process and thinking skills will enable students to respond effectively to a wide range of intellectual challenges (see *Process Skills* beginning on page 13).

Wonder Wise helps teachers utilize time with greater flexibility and creativity. Well–integrated hands–on science activities enable teachers to combine two, three, or four subject areas in a single activity or series of activities. Teachers can integrate curriculum for addressing diversity in students while teaching several subjects in a limited amount of time.

During the 1960s, science educational reformists and the authors of SCIS (Science Curriculum Improvement Study) designed a teaching approach called learning cycles. In evaluating this program, research has repeatedly shown the use of learning cycles to be an effective teaching strategy. *Wonder Wise* has adapted this model and uses hands–on science experiences to connect the child to other elements in cross–curricular activities.

In addition, both basic and higher order thinking skills are addressed in *Wonder Wise* activities. These skills are appropriate for introduction at all elementary levels. Research into the nature of thinking shows that activities commonly associated with higher order thinking skills are not necessarily limited to advanced levels of development. *Wonder Wise* employs Bloom's taxonomy of knowledge levels, a taxonomy that forms a continuum from the basic skills of information gathering and recall to higher order skills of synthesis and analysis (see *Moving Up Bloom's Ladder* page 17).

Learning theorists and developmentalists agree children learn and retain information best when they are actively involved with hands–on experiences. Nationwide surveys indicate teachers need and **want** help making the transition from textbook to experience–based learning. Research further shows teachers want to receive training so they will have the confidence to design meaningful, fun activities that meet curriculum objectives. Educators are becoming frustrated and feel locked into curriculum models that use textbook memorization for learning, and standardized testing for assessment. *Wonder Wise* was designed to break away from traditional approaches, to focus on the processes of learning rather than an end product. Teachers will teach less better, and students will learn, apply, and retain more.

In using the *Wonder Wise* the teacher serves as facilitator of learning stimuli. Teachers ask meaningful, thought–provoking questions that guide the learning experiences. An environment of casual exchange is encouraged to help provide a comfortable classroom climate for sharing ideas, thoughts, and opinions. It is a very different role than that of bearer of all knowledge!

Wonder Wise does not require complicated, expensive materials. It does, however, require a teacher with a respect for logical thinking and a creative imagination to present simple experiments that allow children to think for themselves. The very nature of *Wonder Wise* inspires children to learn and apply what they learn to everyday life.

This program was awarded the Presidential Award of Excellence for Teaching Science and Mathematics and the Christa McAuliffe Award. I hope that the "Wonder Wise Way" will be a winning combination for you and your students.

Karen Cornelsen Heizer

Using Wonder Wise

Lessons in this book will follow a teacher–friendly, consistent format. Look for these components:

Wonder Wise questions to guide the thoughts and open the lesson with inquiry

Concepts states major concepts presented in the learning cycle

Materials lists supplies needed for activities

Discovery Procedure explains the hands–on investigation

Concept Development This section provides suggestions to elicit the concepts and prior student knowledge during the Discovery Procedure. This part of the lesson also includes traditional vocabulary building using responses, textbooks, and audio visual aids. Teachers are strongly encouraged to add their own questions and adapt to meet the needs of their particular students. This stage recognizes the need to teach to the moment.

Facilitator Facts This section provides background information for the teacher. This is **not** to be shared with students initially; these ideas may be generalized by students.

Expansion

provides a hands–on approach to take the first Discovery Procedure a step farther, helping students apply learning to a new situation

Curriculum Connectors

helps the students make connections between the activities and some of these basic subjects:
- Math
- Language Arts
- Social Studies
- Arts and Music
- P.E./Games/Role Play/Creative movement

Trade Books

provides a brief list of popular books that help students bridge science concepts and literature

Assessment Tips

A variety of suggestions are given in specific activities and a general checklist and forms are provided on page 160.

Piggy Back Poem/Song

This section provides closure and will assist the students and teacher in understanding the science concept. The poems also provide a strong language arts connection. (Teachers can use the poems for handwriting lessons and to model creative writing. Classes or individual students could add their own original poems to each activity.)

Wonder Wise Wizards –The Power of Peer Teaching

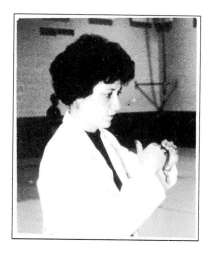

With all the methods of instruction available in the field of education today, I have found one to be most effective for skill mastery...Wonder Wise Wizards! Hands–on experiences along with peer teaching proved to be two strong components. Among the many achievements this program offered, my students strengthened their verbal and higher order thinking skills.

Clearly the peer teaching developed in my students a stronger grasp of science concepts and a deeper appreciation of age appropriate communication skills. Nowhere have I found a learning process with such successful outcomes.

–Shirley Peterson, Teacher
Enid, Oklahoma

One of the strongest components of the *Wonder Wise* curriculum is peer teaching or students teaching students. Students involved in the *Wonder Wise Wizard* program wear baseball caps designed with a cartoon wizard character. The caps help identify the wizards, and provide positive response to the hands-on investigations.

The student wizards spent one or two days a month traveling room to room doing hands–on science activities. The most popular approach was adopting a peer classroom to ensure consistent classroom visitations. This camaraderie provided an environmental comfort zone for both sets of students, thus allowing the learning to flourish.

The homeroom teachers assisted the peer wizards with their questioning techniques and helped them use language developmentally appropriate for their students. The peer teaching wizards follow the three stages of the learning cycle in all visitations. The teacher coached the students in these stages:

Stage 1 – manipulation, exploration, and discovery
Stage 2 – concept development (through inquiry questions)
Stage 3 – expanding the concepts to a new situation or new problem.

All *Wonder Wise* lessons are organized in these three stages. The consistent labeling of the lesson parts makes the activities in this book flexible, adaptable, and appropriate for grades K – 6. If misconceptions become evident, the lessons and schemes can be quickly adapted to meet individual and/or class needs.

My experiences with peer teaching have shown that both sets of students improved in science concepts, process thinking, confidence, retention of concepts, and respect for others. The wizards were surprised by how much they learn when teaching hands–on activities to younger students. It also surprised these older students to see that the younger students had such good basic observation skills. Often, primary students were easily able to make simple but essential observations that were sometimes overlooked by the peer teaching wizards. In interviews with some of these students, many stated they wanted to pursue careers in science fields. Even more surprising were the unexpected announcements by many of the peer students that they loved being a peer wizard so much that they wanted to be teachers when they grow up.

The power of peer teaching is evident when you allow yourself the opportunity to observe and participate in the marvel of this kid magic.

12

Process Skills and Bloom's Ladder

Defining the Process Skills

Process Skill	Definitions
Observe	uses one or more of the senses to identify, notice, watch, examine or inspect an object or event
Classify	performs simple grouping, arranging, sorting, categorizing, comparing, ordering, sequencing, and ranking
Communicate	conveying, information both verbal and written, as well as conveying visual images through graphs, charts, pictures, and diagrams
Record Data	puts information into various written forms; reports, logs, journals, and is able to also perform forms of pictorial labeling, drawing, or sketching
Organize Data	arranges parts into a functioning whole
Interpret Data	can decode, translate, classify, and explain the meaning of information
Infer	proposes interpretations, explanations, and causes of events from collected data; thus can gather, reason, judge, and deduce
Predict	declares possible outcomes in advance, thus can speculate, theorize, anticipate, forecast, and guess
Use Numbers	orders, counts, adds, subtract,s multiplies and divides to quantify data
Measure	can find size, volume, area, mass, weight, or temperature of an object
Replicate Procedure	able to duplicate, model, and imitate
Make Decisions	acts to reach conclusions and resolutions; can also find and judge
Control Variables	recognizes the many factors that affect the outcome of events and their relationships to each other thus having the power to manipulate one variable while controlling others
Formulate Hypotheses	makes educated guesses about objects or events and can test for correctness

Process Skills Scope and Sequence (K–6)

Grade	K	1	2	3	4	5	6
Observing	▨	▨	▨	▨	▨	▨	▨
Classifying and Comparing	▨	▨	▨	▨	▨	▨	▨
Communicating	▨	▨	▨	▨	▨	▨	▨
Recording Data	▨	▨	▨	▨	▨	▨	▨
Organizing Data	▨	▨	▨	▨	▨	▨	▨
Interpreting Data	▨	▨	▨	▨	▨	▨	▨
Inferring and Predicting	▨	▨	▨	▨	▨	▨	▨
Using Numbers & Measuring	▨	▨	▨	▨	▨	▨	▨
Replicating Procedures			▨	▨	▨	▨	▨
Making Decisions					▨	▨	▨
Controlling Variables							▨
Formulating Hypotheses							▨

Integrating Science Process Skills

Science process skills are important in all disciplines.

Science Process Skills	Reading	Math	Social Studies
•Observing	•Observing	•Observing	•Observing
•Classifying	•Comparing •Contrasting •Ordering	•Sorting •Sequencing •Ordering •Patterning	•Comparing ideas and cultures
•Inferring	•Inferring cause and effect	•Inferring •Deducing •Gathering	•Inferring
•Measuring	•Time frames as story elements	•Weight •Volume •Mass •Size •Area •Temperature	•Time frames and time lines on historical events
•Using numbers	•Sequencing and story order: first, next, then, last	•Ordering •Counting •Adding, subtracting, multiplying and dividing	•Ordering of events •Figuring mileage •Interpreting maps, graphs, charts and tables
•Predicting	•Predicting story outcomes, problems, and solutions	•Predicting •Estimating •Calculating and computing	•Proposing possible outcomes based on past events
•Collecting data	•Taking notes	•Organizing and interpreting data	•Organizing and interpreting data from maps, charts and pictures
•Interpreting data	•Determining cause and effect •Organizing information	•Analyzing •Solving •Explaining •Classifying	•Interpreting data •Decoding charts and maps •Recognizing variables
•Communicating results	•Logically arranging information •Writing •Discussing	•Conveying information numerically •Graphing •Charting	•Map making •Graphing information •Writing and discussing

Moving Up Bloom's Ladder

Descriptive words designed for teachers to aid in recognizing various levels of cognitive learning. The aim is to move students from lower levels to higher levels of cognitive development.

- Judge •Consider
- Conclude •Decide
- Evaluate •Weigh
- Criticize •Determine
- Appraise •Rate
- Select •Predict

- Originate •Develop •Compose
- Role play •Produce •Design
- Plan •Create •Formulate •Invent
- Modify •Construct •Manipulate
- Assemble

- Discriminate •Compare •Diagram
- Differentiate •Experiment •Put into lists
- Describe •Classify •Analyze •Solve
- Categorize •Subdivide •Deduce
- Contrast •Question

- Apply •Use •Organize •Restructure •Solve
- Generalize •Classify •Practice •Demonstrate
- Choose •Transfer •Dramatize •Construct

- Translate •Restate •Rearrange •Give examples
- Report •Discuss •Transform •Demonstrate
- Infer •Generalize •Describe •Interpret •Illustrate
- Explain •Summarize •Write observations

- Define •Recognize •Match •Memorize •Distinguish
- Identify •Name •Label •Recall •Select •List

Physical Science

Squeezable Squid

Have you ever **wondered why** some objects float while other objects sink?

Concepts

Air pressure, bouyancy, displacement, gravity, and air compression

Materials

2–liter bottles, glass droppers, water, and *Maxi Tube Squids* (found in fishing/bait supply section at local stores).

Discovery Procedure

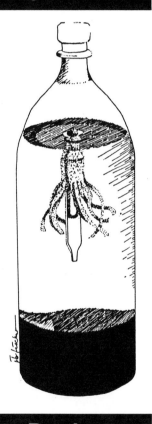

Have students fill the 2–liter bottle full of water. They will also need to slide a plastic squid over the plastic top of the dropper. You may need to add some baby oil or petroleum jelly to keep from tearing the delicate squid. Have students float the glass drop-per (now a squid) in the top of the bottle. A clear dropper will allow students to observe the compress-ing of air and the increase of water level. If students have trouble floating the dropper, have them fill the dropper one–third to one–half full of water and test in a jar of water. Air must remain in part of the dropper.

Make sure the students put the cap of the 2–liter bottle on tightly. As students squeeze the bot-tle the squid will start to sink. (It will take some prac-tice along with good, strong hand muscles). Allow students to experiment and play with the squid diver. Have students name the squid and talk to it. Does it follow their voice directions, like: "Sink Squiggly!" "Float Squiggly!" "Stay in the middle! Dance!" etc? Encourage creativity.

Concept Development

✪What can you see happening to the diver/squid?
✪What does it do when you first squeeze the bottle?
✪Do you notice any changes in the water or the squid?
✪What pushes the squid/diver up and down?
✪Where does this material go (or transfer to)?
✪What do you think causes the dropper to sink or float?
✪Can you find a way to make the squid stay in the middle of the bottle? Try it!

Facilitator Facts

The pressure you put on the sides of the bottle is transferred to the air inside the dropper. You can see the level of the water in the dropper go up as you squeeze. The water level inside the dropper rises as it pushes the air above into a smaller space. The dropper thus becomes less buoyant and sinks. Equalizing pressure, and compressing air is the cause of it all.

Expansions

•Have students use colored water in the 2–liter bottle and remove the squid from the dropper. Then repeat the experiment as before. This color difference will show the water exchange in the dropper.

•Students can also leave the top off the bottle but must predict what will happen when they squeeze. Then let them try it!

Curriculum Connectors

Math

✪How high must the water rise in the dropper before the squid sinks? Predict and then check your answer.

Language Arts

Have students make a list of "squ" words.
Encourage students to write a story about how their squid moves *when the pressure is on.*

Assessment Tips

Have students draw a picture of what they think happened to the dropper to make it sink.
Have students discuss their ideas and explain their drawings to each other.

Piggy Back Poem

The Squeeze

Compressing the air
By giving a squeeze,
Sends the squid to the bottom
As fast as you please.

Spinnards

Have you ever **wondered why** a maple or sycamore seed spins as it falls through the air?

Concepts

Air, gravity, air resistance, and rotative motion

Materials

Prepared chart (see following page), a *Spinnard Pattern* (Worksheets 1, 2, 3, or 4) for each student, paper clips

Discovery Procedure

Cut out your choice of paper spinnard and explain to your students that the spinnard is unhappy because it can only *float* to the ground. Demonstrate this by letting go of the spinnard. Discuss what the students observe. Spinnard does not want to just *float* – it wants to *spin* (just like its name).
✪Can you think of ways to make it spin?

Go to the chart on the board and see what the Four Wise Cousins advise. (Students will predict which cousin they think gives the best advice.) Before experimenting, read the following story. This is a generic story; be creative and add your own ideas.

$\mathcal{S}$pinnard was a special creature with a desire to spin instead of just float in the air like all the other creatures around him. Its name was Spinnard, and thus it wanted desperately to do just that – to spin, not float! It was very puzzled on just how to solve its problem. Spinnard had four very wise cousins, so it decided to call them all in for a family conference. After gathering the four wise cousins together Spinnard said, "Cousins, I have been trying and trying to spin, but I just cannot seem to get it right. Can you give me some wise advice?" (Refer to chart on next page.)

"Oh yes," the first cousin said. "Just put on heavy shoes (paper clip) and hold your hands up. That will work; I'm absolutely *sure* of it."

"No, no," said the second wise cousin. "Go ahead and keep those shoes on. But you must *also* fold both your arms *forward.* "

"Oh no," the third wise cousin said. "You have it all wrong. You must indeed keep those shoes on, but you must put one arm *forward* and one arm *back.*"

"No, no, no," responded the fourth (and supposedly wisest) cousin. "You take those shoes *off* and keep your arms straight and remember 'if you think you can - YOU CAN!' You see, it's positive thinking that makes you spin."

Using the chart form on the following page, ask students to make predictions and place their name under the cousin who they think gave the best advice. (Post-it® notes work great here.) Read the graph and make comparisons of the different guesses. Students then experiment with their own Spinnard following the cousins' advice in sequential order. Some teacher guidance is required.

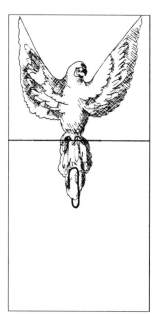 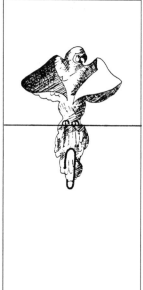 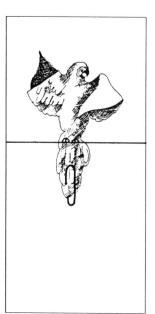 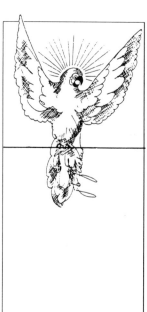

COUSIN 1	COUSIN 2	COUSIN 3	COUSIN 4
SHOES ON *and* ARMS UP	SHOES ON *but* FOLD BOTH ARMS FORWARD	SHOES ON *but* ONE ARM FORWARD ONE ARM BACK	SHOES OFF *and* JUST THINK POSITIVELY

Concept Development

✪Which cousin gave the best advice?
✪What made this cousin's spinner advice the best?
✪What have you seen in the real world that spins?
✪Do any of these things you've seen have one arm forward and one arm back?
✪Why do you think a paper clip is needed on the spinner?

Encourage students to compare and discuss their findings in relation to the graph.

Facilitator Facts

In order to move, everything that travels above the ground or water must push air out of its way. The paper clip adds weight which assists the spinning movement downward. The motion of a spinnard blade operates through air on the principles of action/reaction and air resistance. The faster the spinner moves, the more air the arm pushes. As the arm pushes in one direction, the air pushes back in the other direction. Air force is less than gravity so the spinner gently floats to the ground. The result: a *Spinnard*.

Expansion

Challenge students to make Spinnard spin in the opposite direction (reverse arms). Make spinnards out of different types of paper and see which one spins the fastest and slowest.

24

Curriculum Connectors

Math	The predicting, graphing, counting, and interpreting of data provide the math connection.

Language Arts	Have students write their own creative story on how Spinnard solved its spinning problems.

Art	Have students cut out the spinnards and use markers and crayons to give their Spinnard a personality and style. Encourage students to invent their own spinnard pattern or product.

Trade Books

Air and Flight - Neil
Air - Lloyd
The Old Lady Who Wasn't Afraid of Anything - Williams
The Ghost Eye Tree - Martin
Feel The Wind - Dorras
The Air Around Us - Frisky
Air Is All Around You - Branley

Assessment Tips	Assessing this activity includes teacher observations and student involvement during the experimental stage of predicting and finding the best spinner. Student communication of observations and findings will help assess their levels of understanding.

Piggy Back Poem

Around and Down

Spinnard found a paper clip,
Which gave it extra weight.
Spinnard held its arms like chopper blades
And moved and spun just great!

Parrot Spinnard

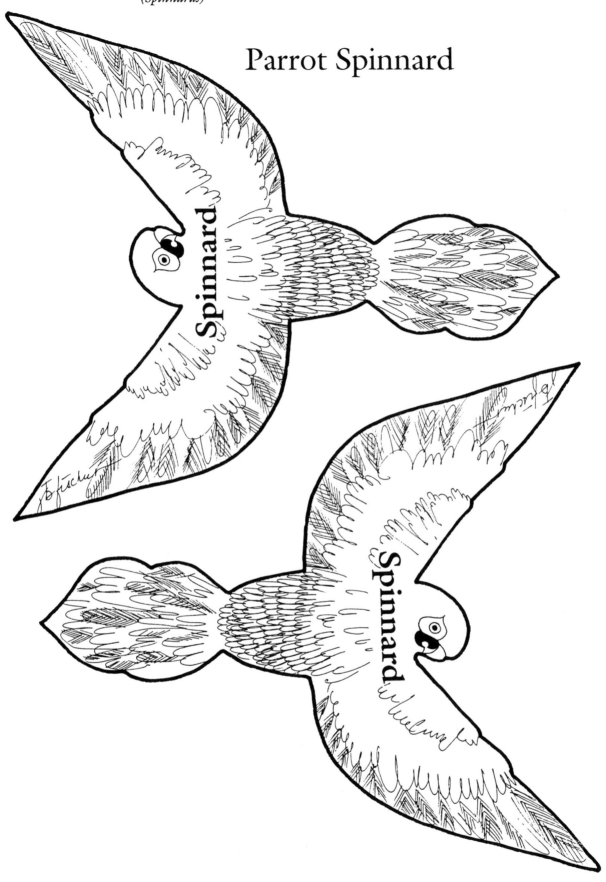

Spinnard

Spinnard

Rabbit Spinnard

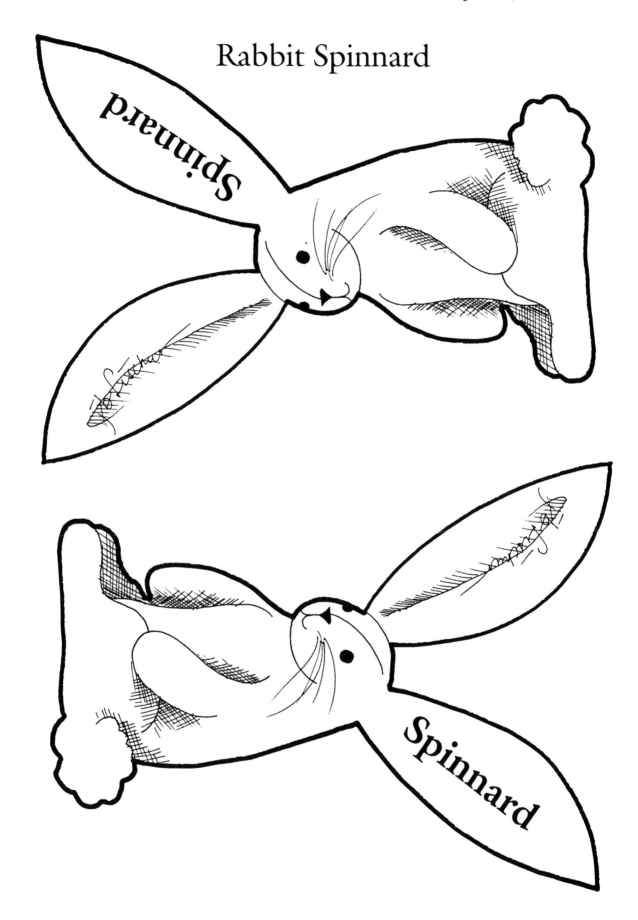

Ghost Spinnard

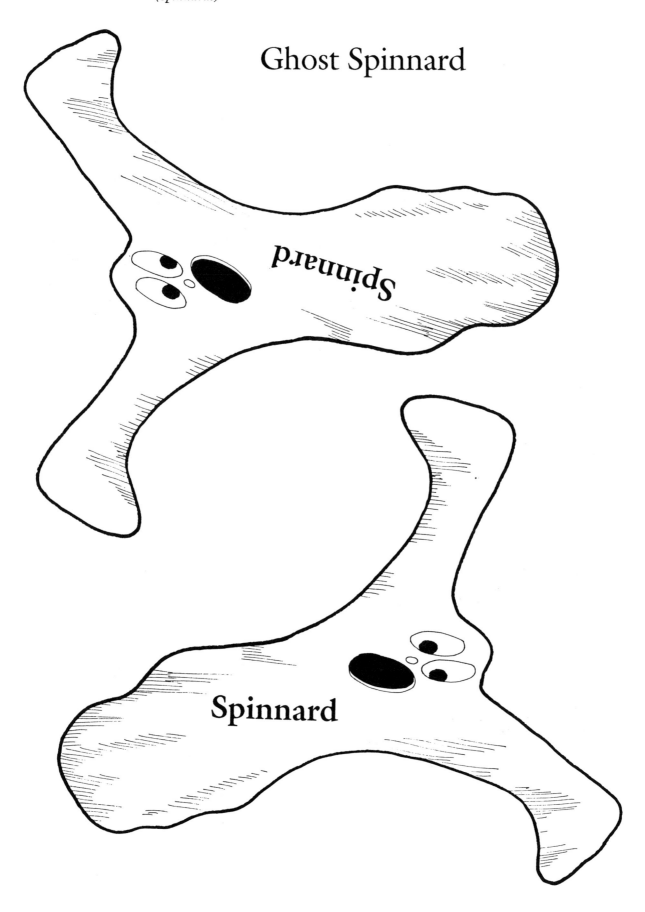

Spinnard

Spinnard

Teddy Bear Spinnard

Walking Water

Wonder Wise

Have you ever **wondered why** water travels in a linear path? Think of water hoses, kitchen sinks, drinking fountains, and even water falls. Why doesn't the water just splatter in all directions?

Concepts

Surface tension and gravity

Materials

String/yarn cut two or three feet long, water, and two large cups/containers (one to catch the water and one to pour), and an outdoor area

Discovery Procedure

Give each pair of students a string and two containers; one empty, the other half full of water. Tell students they must find some way to get the water from one container to the other using the string. Students should try to accomplish this with little or no water spills.

The students should experiment and problem solve with little guidance from the teacher. Here are a few hints to give the students as they experiment:
✪Do you think water can travel in a path?
✪What could you do with the string to make it a path for the water?
✪What happens when the string gets wet?

If students have trouble holding the string in the water containers, have them tie a washer or nut on the end of the string, tape the end of the string securely inside the bottom of the containers, or tie the ends of the string to the handles of the containers.

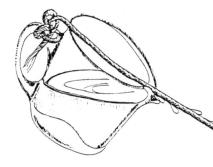

Concept Development

✪Could you get the water to travel on the string?
✪Did you have any spills?
✪When did the water stay on the string best?
✪What helped the water cling to the string?
✪What was the best way for you to get the water into the cup using the string?
✪Why do you think water sticks to water?
✪What made the water stick and follow the line of the string?
✪Where have you noticed water sticking to water in your daily life? (Examples: dew on spider webs, rain on cars, water running off wet hair).

Facilitator Facts

Water molecules hug together tightly. This clinging action forms an elastic, tube–like skin, inside which the water flows; in this case, the wet string sits inside the tube skin. This elastic skin which water and other liquids form is called *surface tension*. Water sticks to water (cohesion). Therefore, it will not follow a string without the string first being wet. When the string is wet, the water will follow the path in a smooth motion. Surface tension accounts for why rain drops are round, why wet hair sticks to your head, and why water insects can walk on water.

Expansion

Have students set up three or four different string paths from elevated water–pouring containers to ground–level empty containers. Some strings should be dry and some wet. Have the string paths crisscross each other. (You may want to add weights to the ends of the strings to hold them in position). Predict which path(s) most of the water will follow. Now pour the water slowly and observe the magic of water "walking" along string paths.

Curriculum Connectors

Math

These activities integrate math through counting, predicting, measuring, and problem solving.

Social Studies

Explain to students that in the history of space flight, the concept of surface tension has been vital in the understanding of micro–gravity; liquids cannot be stored in open containers because they run **up** the walls of the space capsule!

Trade Books

Where Does Water Come From? - Vance
The Magic School Bus at the Water Works - Cole

Assessment Tips

Students' understanding can be assessed by having them define water tension and name three to five places where they have seen surface tension at work in their everyday life. Or simply have students explain what they have observed in their own words. The sophistication of any explanation can be used as a formative assessment.

Piggy Back Poem

Sticking Together

ATTENTION, droplets, gather 'round,
Draw those ranks in tight.
We're taking a trip down a string,
And THIS time we'll do it right!

This time the string will be wet,
So we'll have a much better hold,
And slowly advance together,
The many, the proud, and the bold!

32

Color Mystery

Wonder Wise

Have you ever **wondered why** we see so many colors? How do they all form? Where do you think rainbows get their colors?

Concepts

Chemistry, primary and secondary colors

Materials

White ice cube trays or egg cartons, eyedroppers, squeeze bottles or containers of water with red, blue, and yellow food coloring added

Discovery Procedure

All students or groups will need an ice cube tray. Have students fill three of the cube sections with one of each of these colors of dyed water: red, blue, and yellow. The remaining sections remain empty. Students may now move one color at a time to an empty section using the eyedropper. Make certain students do not mix the original three primary color samples; all mixing should occur in the remaining cube sections. Give students free exploration time to move primary colors into various combinations . Have them record the new colors they create using only the three primary colors.

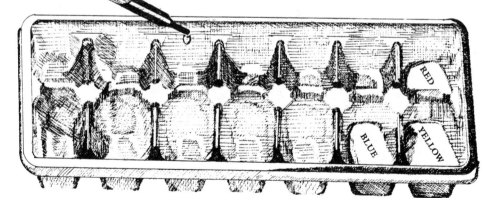

Concept Development

✪What new colors did you create?
✪How many new colors did you create?
✪What seems to make colors lighter?
✪What did you do to make them appear darker?
✪What were the three beginning colors ?
✪Are colors important to you?
✪Why do you think the color mixtures of purple, green, and orange are called secondary colors?

Red, blue, and yellow are the primary colors. When mixed they form the secondary colors of purple, green, and orange. An artist can create just about any color necessary for a palette using only red, blue, and yellow.

Expansion

Give each student or group a mirror and a clear plastic container half full of water. Working outdoors, ask the students to find a rainbow using the mirror, sunshine, and the container of water. They need to stand so the sun is behind them.

On a sunny day anyone can see a rainbow in the spray of a garden hose. The same thing happens when a natural rainbow appears in the sky. The water in the sky, necessary for the rainbow's formation, comes from a distant rain shower. Ask students to look for the primary colors in the rainbow.

Name and list in order the primary and secondary colors as they appear in your rainbow. It might be helpful to students to teach them the acronym name of Roy G. Biv to aid them in remembering the rainbow color sequence (**r**ed, **o**range, **y**ellow, **g**reen, **b**lue, **i**ndigo, and **v**iolet).

Curriculum Connectors

Math

Students can now use mathematic statements/equations to help translate the color formulas such as:

$$R + Y = O \quad \text{or;} \quad \text{Red} + \text{Yellow} = \text{Orange}$$

Help students find as many mathematical combinations as possible.

Communicating color combinations can be done using the following geometric color wheels. Have students draw and color various combinations:

Example:

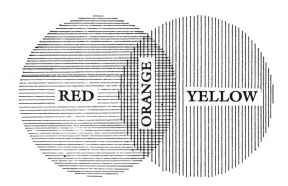

$$R + Y = O$$

Have students solve the following problem:
✪If you were an artist with only enough money to buy three colors, what would they be?
✪Would you need to buy white?

Social Studies

Make a large rainbow chart and have students place their names on their favorite color. Make sure your rainbow follows the Roy G. Biv color scheme to help reinforce the sequence of rainbow colors.

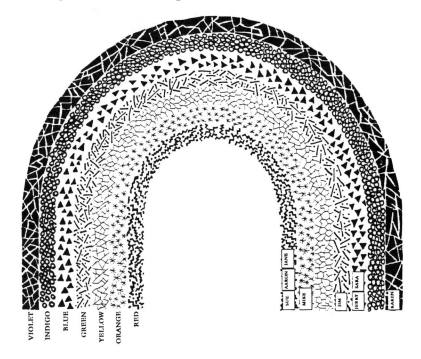

Trade Books

Hugo and the Man who Stole Colors - Ross
Colors, Colors all Around - Scott
Put Me in the Zoo - Lopshire
Once Upon a Rainbow - Lewis

Assessment Tips

Ask students to perform the task of creating the colors orange, green, and purple using only an ice cube tray of red, blue, and yellow colored water. Have students communicate, write, and demonstrate the color combinations needed to produce these secondary colors.

Piggy Back Poem

Classy Colors

By mixing the primary colors,
You can get those in between.
Mixing red, yellow, and blue,
You get purple, orange, and green!

The beauty of a rainbow,
Shows just how this is so.
Where the primary colors overlap,
The secondary colors show.

To remember the order of colors,
The rainbow has to give,
Memorize this fellow's name:
Roy G. Biv!

Skittle® Scatters

Concepts

Investigative science, observing, classifying, inferring, communicating, measuring, number sense, predicting, interpreting data, and defining operationally

Materials

Red 2.17oz. bag of Skittle® candies, pencil, *Skittle® Scatter* (Worksheet 2), *Skittle® Search* (Worksheet 1), and *Skittle® Sense/Sum Skittles®* (Worksheet 3)

Discovery Procedure

Ask each student to bring a small, unopened bag of Skittles® to class. Ask them to make a prediction of how many candies they think are in the bag. They should record their answer on *Skittle® Search* (Worksheet 1)

Next students should be allowed time to open their bags and scatter their Skittles® on a clean, flat surface examining each candy closely. Give all students copies of *Skittle® Scatter* (Worksheet 2) and encourage them to sort candies according to color.

Time should now be taken to complete the remaining questions on Worksheet 1.

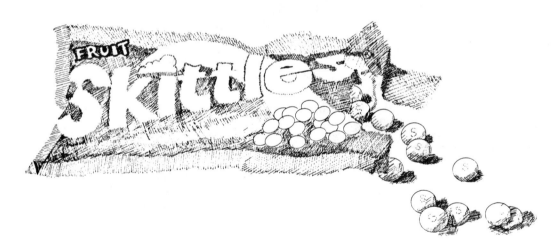

Concept Development

✪Were you surprised at the difference between your prediction and the actual amount of candies in the bag?

✪What colors appeared the least, and which the most?

✪How could we collect the class results? (chart or graph)

✪What did you learn from doing your Skittle® Search?

Facilitator Facts

In early developmental stages students learn best from direct experiences in which they observe, describe, sort, and organize objects. More advanced cognitive levels are reached by classifying, testing, experimenting, and evaluating relationships between objects.

Expansion

Have students design a way to do subtraction with their Skittles®. Also, have them find additional ways to sort their candies. Students can assemble their candies into patterns, as well as sequencing them by color from the most candies to the least candies.

Curriculum Connectors

Math

Using *Skittle® Sense/Sum Skittles®* (Worksheet 3), have students answer these questions:
✪What math symbols did you use to show greater than, lesser than, and equal to?
✪Will the results of all the problems from each bag of candy be different?
✪How did you do multiplication, division and grouping on this worksheet?

Language Arts

As a class, have students write a friendly letter to the Skittle® company (Mars, Inc., Hackettstown, NJ 07840) suggesting they include more of the_____ color of Skittles®. Make sure the letter gives three reasons why the students want to see an increase in this particular color. Make certain the letter follows all the rules of a friendly letter style.

Assessment Tips

Written evaluation can be taken from the worksheets. Facilitator will need to monitor closely as all Skittle® bags will not be packaged the same.
Teacher observation of student involvement is a valid assessment.

Skittle® Search

1. Do not open your bag yet!
   Guess how many Skittles® are in your closed bag._____

2. Open your bag, and count the candies.
   How many candies are actually in your bag?_____

3. What was the difference between your prediction and the
   actual number?_____

4. Write the total number of Skittles® in each color set:
   Green =_____(G)
   Purple =_____(P)
   Orange =_____(O)
   Red =_____(R)
   Yellow =_____(Y)

5. Use the signs (>, <, or =) to show the relationship in each color set:
   G___P   R___G   P___R
   P___O   G___Y   P___Y
   R___Y   G___O   O___R
   O___Y

6. Do these Skittle® color addition problems:
   R+P=____   P+O=____
   R+O=____   P+Y=____
   R+Y=____   P+G=____
   R+G=____   O+Y=____
   Y+G=____

7. Put 16 Skittles® in a pile in front of you.
   How many piles of 4 can you make?_____
   How many are left over?_____
   How many piles of 8 can you make?_____
   How many are left over?_____
   How many piles of 5 can you make?_____
   How many are left over?_____
   Put 2 in your mouth. How many are left?

Organize the contents of your bag into color piles.

Skittle® Scatter

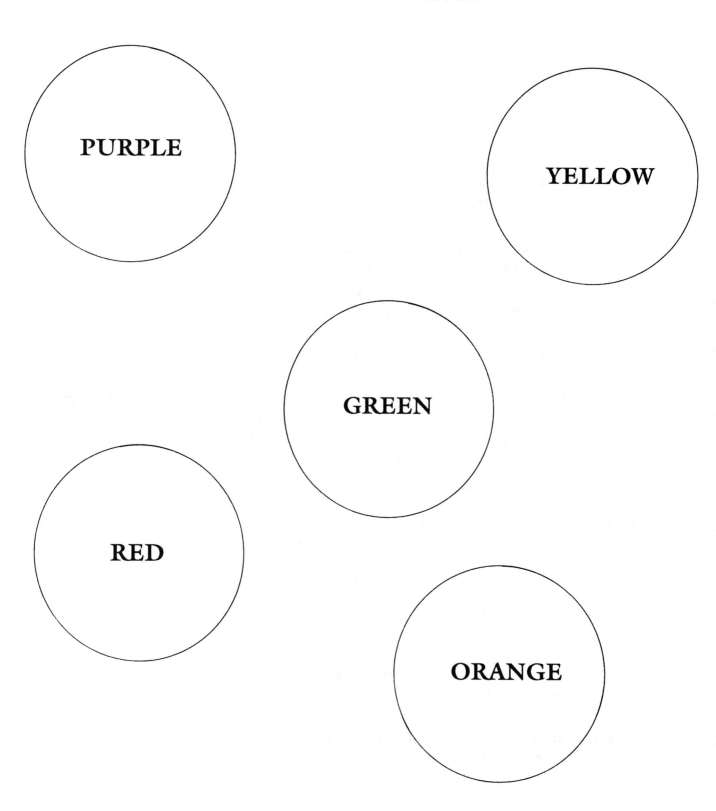

Skittle® Sense

Skittles® are said to be made of real fruit juices. Predict the flavor of each color, then taste each, and record its fruit flavor:

	Prediction	Actual
YELLOW	_____	_____
RED	_____	_____
PURPLE	_____	_____
GREEN	_____	_____
ORANGE	_____	_____

Sum Skittles®

Use your Skittles® as non–standard measurement tools on a balance scale. Use these candies to measure the following classroom objects:

Pencil=_____Candies

Crayon=_____Candies

Eraser=_____Candies

Chalk=_____Candies

Paper clip=_____Candies

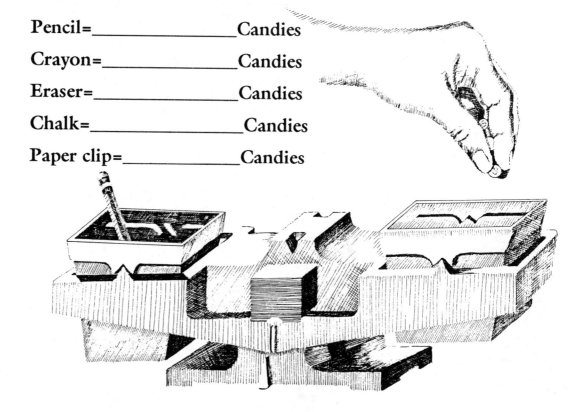

Baffled By Bubbles

Wonder Wise

Have you ever **wondered why** a bubble forms and what holds it together?

Concepts

Air, surface tension, and wind

Materials

Joy® or Dawn® dishwashing detergent; two tablespoons of glycerin, Karo® syrup or gelatin (these substances slow the evaporation of water and add strength to the bubble solution); one-gallon container; 14 cups of warm water; warm, humid day and a large outdoor area

Discovery Procedure

Mix two cups of dishwashing detergent, 14 cups of water and two tablespoons of one of the following substances: glycerin, Karo® syrup, or gelatin. Stir gently. If you wish, add extra soap to the solution for larger bubbles. Let this solution stand at room temperature for a day or two. To help the bubbles last longer, refrigerate this solution for a few minutes before using. The water in your geographical location will vary the solution. Do not be afraid to experiment; science is experimentation. For best results, have students perform the following activity on a rainy, humid day. The more moisture in the air, the longer the bubbles will last.

Set up stations and rotate students.
Caution: Make sure students *blow out* and do *not* *suck in* the bubble solutions. Teacher may need to explain the difference. Each station should contain bubble solutions and tools for experimenting with bubbles. Varying the compositions of the solutions at each station will increase the challenge of the procedure.

Students can make bubble blowers from almost anything: straws, fingers, strawberry baskets, hangers, tin horns, funnels, paper cups or juice cans with the ends removed.

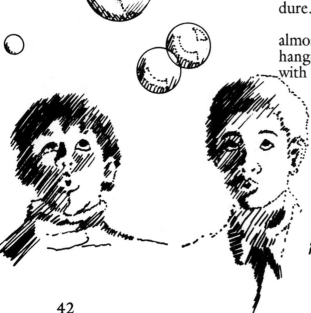
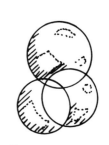

42

Concept Development

✪What do you think makes bubbles form?
✪Do you think all the soapy solutions are the same?
✪How do you know?
✪Why do you think bubbles move in the air without you touching them (and what happens to the bubbles if you do touch them)?
✪What causes bubbles to move in the air?
✪What delays the popping of some bubbles?
✪Can you catch a bubble and hold it in your hand?
✪Is there a special way to catch a soapy bubble without breaking it?
✪What happens when you touch a bubble with a wet hand? dry hand?
✪Could you keep a bubble forever?
✪What did the bubble leave on your hand when it popped?
✪ No matter what you use to blow the bubble, what general shape does the bubble usually take?
✪Where do you see bubbles in your everyday world?
✪How might a natural bubble beneath the earth cause an earthquake?

Facilitator Facts

Air is inside the bubble. You can see the bubble, but you cannot see the air. You can see through the air in the bubble in the same way you can see through the air all around you. Soapy bubbles are a type of air bubble. When you blow a soapy bubble, you put air inside a soap and water skin.

Water has skin due to something called surface tension. This surface tension is created by the molecular structure of water as its molecules meet the molecules of the air. Sometimes water skin will pull so tightly that the bubble will break.

Soapy bubbles can last longer in the air than plain water bubbles because the soap weakens the water molecules and the skin becomes increasingly flexible.

You can make bubbles stay up in the air longer by blowing on them. This air flow is called wind.

Expansions

• Put a clear plastic container, filled with water, on an overhead projector. Add objects like rocks, a brick, erasers, plants, corks, baking soda, etc. Observe for bubbles.
✪What do you think causes these bubbles to appear?
✪Where do you think the bubbles in ponds and lakes come from?

• Have students find a way to blow a bubble within another bubble.

• Add sugar to the solution. Students should describe any new observations.

Curriculum Connectors

Math

Have students test different bubble recipes. Vary the combinations of the detergent, water, glycerin, corn syrup or sugar in different containers. Write the recipe on the label of each container. Have students use a bubble wand and blow bubbles from each mixture. Count or use a stopwatch to see which recipe makes the longest lasting bubbles. Record student findings.

Language Arts

Brainstorm and assign a creative story about what it would be like to have the only bubble in the world.
✪How would you keep it forever?
✪Would you ever be able to give it away or sell it?
✪Why or why not?
✪Could life exist within a bubble? You may want to discuss the Biosphere experiment, or the boy who, for medical reasons, had to live in a type of bubble.

Art

Add food coloring to the bubble solution. Put this solution in a shallow pie tin. Give each student a straw to blow bubbles in the tin. Have them observe. Now have students cut a small hole in a piece of white paper and put the straw through the hole as they place the paper over the top of the pie tin. Again have students blow bubbles. Encourage students to predict what will happen when the bubbles come in contact with the paper. Bubble art!

Social Studies

Introduce the Danish scientist Niels Henrik David Bohr. He was awarded the Nobel Prize for physics and is most notably remembered for his knowledge of surface tension in the droplet model. This model treats the nucleus of an atom as if it were a water droplet held together by its surface tension. (Bohr was also a pioneer in the development of atomic theory.)

Trade Book

Soap Bubble Magic - Simon

Assessment Tips

The student data collection and oral communication in reporting three to five observations made during the experiments will give information and clues on basic understanding and levels of processing the bubble experiment.

Piggy Back Poem

Bubble Beauty

Gently blow some air into
A soap and water *skin*.
Bubbles feel the waiting sky
Like magic, again and again.

The speed of the air blown in,
Makes bubbles large or small.
But no matter the size, or the path they take,
We love them one and all.

clp

Solids, Liquids, Gases and Something In Between

Discovery Procedure

This will be a teacher directed discovery. The teacher says to students, "Today we are going to discover something important about objects all around us that make up our world. Everything that takes up space is made up of this special mystery word. We are going to discover what this word is, and how it relates to objects in the world." At this early stage of the learning cycle it is important that the word *matter* not be used. Lead the students to discover its meaning.

SOLIDS

Teacher will direct students to find a solid object in the classroom and hold it in their hand.
✪Was it easy to find a solid?
✪How does the solid feel?
✪Does it keep its shape when you press on it?
✪Will it always stay in its exact solid form?
The facilitator should demonstrate the ability of solids to change their shape by:
(1) crushing a piece of chalk underfoot, and
(2) crumbling a tissue.
Make certain students see the chalk and tissue in their original forms, and that they agree on their solidity. The facilitator needs to explain that some solids do change shape, but that they do so using forces outside themselves.
✪Do solids have weight? Show how you would weigh a solid. (Students should use the scales/balance with the classroom objects they had previously picked out.) Have students record the weights on the board or a classroom chart.

LIQUIDS

Now the facilitator directs the students' attention to another type of substance.
✪Is water a solid?
✪Why do you think it is not a solid?
✪Do you believe that water is a liquid?
✪Are liquids wet?
✪Is water wet?

•Hand students small containers of water and tell them to touch the water itself.
✪How does it feel?
✪What do you see?

•Distribute different shaped containers to the students (cylinders, cups, balloons, bottles, dishes, seas shells, etc.)
✪What do you think will happen if you pour the water into a different shaped container?
✪Will the shape of the water change?
✪What shape does the water form? (the shape of the container)

GASES

Finally students will discover another type of substance that is not so easy to see.
✪What do you predict this last substance will be?

•Give each student a balloon or bag.
✪Is this object a solid or a liquid?

•Instruct students to blow into the balloon/bag.
✪What happened?
✪What did you put into the bag?
✪Can you see the air or gas you just added to the bag?
✪How do you know it is there?
✪Do gases take the shape of their containers?
Have students experiment with this concept by reshaping their balloon/bag.
✪Do you think most gases are invisible?
✪Can you squeeze a gas?
Have students try, then discuss the results.

Concept Development

✪What are the three forms of matter you just discovered?
✪How are they all different?
✪Do they have things in common?
✪Can you think of a way you can change water into a solid and into a gas? (ice and steam)

Facilitator Facts

Everything that takes up space is made up of matter; solids, liquids, or gases. Rock is a solid, water is a liquid, and air is a gas, but they do not always have to be. Given the right conditions, each can change into another state of matter. It has to do with tiny particles called atoms and molecules. Heating, boiling, melting, cooling, freezing, and mixing can change the bonds between these tiny particles. These changed conditions can break atoms apart or pull them together thus changing the condition of the matter.

Molecules move around like a troop of soldiers in a solid, dancers on a crowded dance floor in a liquid, and like popping corn moving far apart at high speeds in all directions in a gas.

Expansion

Allow students free exploration time and tell students or cooperative groups they will now go on a Matter Treasure Hunt – preferably outside. Students will collect samples of the three forms of matter. Ask them to share and tell about their findings. Remind students that matter should not be hard for them to find because everything that takes up space is made of matter.

Curriculum Connectors

Language Arts/Math

First read the story *Oobleck* by Dr. Seuss. Then have students or groups make oobleck by doing the following:

Measure three tablespoons of corn starch into a paper cup. Add three tablespoons of green colored water and stir. (Students may need to slightly adjust amount of water so mixture can be poured slowly.) Have students comment on what they observe as they mix together this solid and liquid.To help students classify the discoveries and characteristics of this and other substances, they can use *Matter of Facts* (Worksheet 1).
✪Do you have matter that is a solid or a liquid?
✪Which properties of each does the oobleck have?

•Have students place a metal, wood or plastic object on their mixture. They should explain and record what they observe.

•Have them place the mixture in their hand.
✪Can you bend it?
✪Can you break it?

•Have students try to cut the mixture with a stick or their finger.
✪Can your mixture be cut?
✪What happens to the "cut" after a few minutes?

•Have students hit the mixture in their hand with the palm of their other hand.
✪Does the mixture splatter?

•Students should rub some of the mixture between their fingers.
✪Is the mixture wet?

Additional Facilitator Fact

The starch mixed with water will flow like a liquid, break into pieces like a solid, will powder when rubbed, will withstand shocks but not support weight. This substance seems to break the Newtonic theory that all matter fits into one of the three states of matter. It seems that there are always exceptions to any rule in science. A young child in class once referred to this substance as a *rule breaker*. I think Newton would be happy with her discovery and terminology.

Social Studies

Inform students that over 2,000 years ago, many natural philosophers thought that matter could be divided into four basic elements: earth, water, air, and fire. Are modern divisions of matter really so different? (solids, liquids and gases)

Role Play

Students can act out matter molecule movements in the following ways:

Solid – Students march together in a tight military formation.

Liquid – Students dance in a gliding fashion in a crowded area of the room.

Gas – Students spread out and move fast bumping into and bouncing off of each other. ***Remind students to be gentle so no one gets hurt.***

The teacher can also suggest specific types of matter, such as Rock (solid), Water (liquid), and Air (gas).

Trade Books

Oobleck - Dr. Seuss
The Quicksand Book - De Paola
Why Can't You Unscramble an Egg? - Cobb
Changing Things - Kerrod
Matter - Wilkin

Assessment Tips

Process assessment of this activity can be through teacher observation during the role playing activity and student communication from the Matter Treasure Hunt.

Product assessment can be evaluated from ***Matter of Facts*** (Worksheet 1). The teacher may set up various items in a performance center to see if students can classify and group the items as solids, liquids, and gases.

Piggy Back Poem

What's the Matter?

Solids have a definite shape,
And can be easily felt and seen.
They take up space and carry weight,
I'm sure you know what I mean!

Liquids, it's still plain to see,
Have weight and take up space.
But they're wet, will pour, and flow
To just about any place!

Gases are mostly invisible,
Can spread or be compressed.
All three of these are *matter*,
As I'm sure you've already guessed!

dp

Matter of Facts

SOLID

____takes up space

____has weight

____has a definite shape

____has shape unless an outside change is forced on it

LIQUID

____takes up space

____has weight

____is wet

____takes the shape of the container it is in

____will pour and form level surface

GAS

____takes up space

____takes the shape of its container

____changes its shape

____is usually invisible, but takes up space (like air inside
a bubble)

____can be squeezed and compressed

____can spread indefinitely

My unidentified substance seems to be a _____

because_____

_____

_____

_____

Earth and Environmental Science

Paper Path to the Planets

Wonder Wise

Have you ever **wondered why** we cannot see all the planets from Earth? How far away can the planets really be?

Concepts

Scale model, solar system, size, distance, and planet sequence

Materials

•One full roll of toilet tissue,
•Two: marbles, ping–pong balls, tennis balls
•One: golf ball, basketball, volleyball, beach ball
(Substitute balloons if balls cannot be found.)
•Nine index cards labeled; Mercury, Venus, Earth, Mars, Jupiter, Saturn, Uranus, Neptune, and Pluto

Discovery Procedure

Students will need to collect or bring in the balls listed in the materials section above. After the balls have been gathered, have students carefully roll out 300 sheets of toilet tissue. Lay it out on the ground, in a hallway, classroom, or gymnasium; a straight line is best. Students will place the beach ball at one end of the toilet paper path. Students will measure from the beach ball which represents the sun. Have students map out the solar system using the chart below, adding the index cards to label the planets.

Adapting this activity to an indoor hallway or classroom is easily done by taping the 300 sheets to a wall, and cutting the planets out of construction paper approximating the size of the ball models. Students can add creative solar system art to give added visual interest. This makes a wonderful class reference chart.

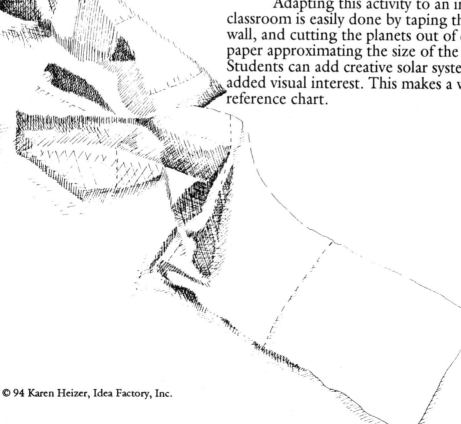

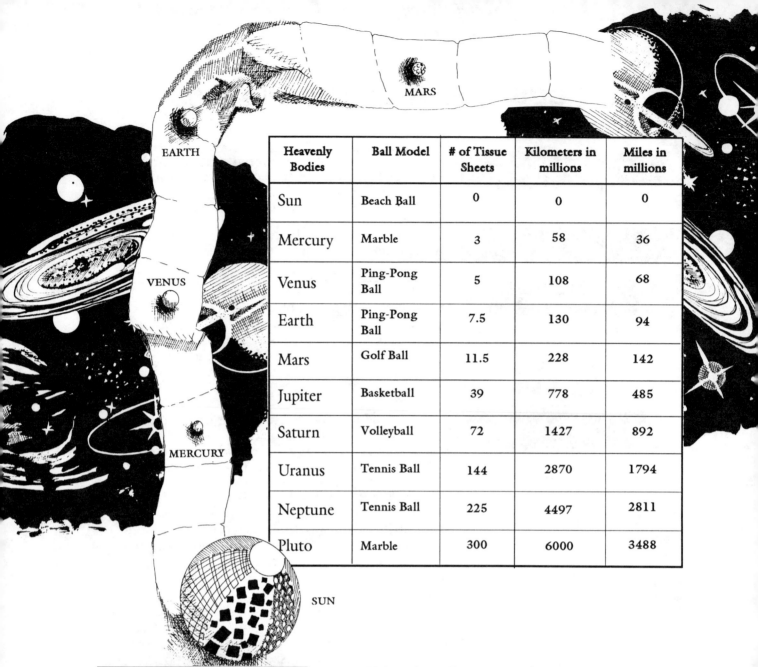

Heavenly Bodies	Ball Model	# of Tissue Sheets	Kilometers in millions	Miles in millions
Sun	Beach Ball	0	0	0
Mercury	Marble	3	58	36
Venus	Ping-Pong Ball	5	108	68
Earth	Ping-Pong Ball	7.5	130	94
Mars	Golf Ball	11.5	228	142
Jupiter	Basketball	39	778	485
Saturn	Volleyball	72	1427	892
Uranus	Tennis Ball	144	2870	1794
Neptune	Tennis Ball	225	4497	2811
Pluto	Marble	300	6000	3488

Concept Development

Using the toilet paper solar system model ask the following of your students:

❂What do you see?

❂How many sheets of tissue are between each planet?

❂Are the distances the same between each planet?

❂Why do you think we cannot see all the planets from Earth?

❂Which planet is farthest from the sun?

❂Which planet is closest to the sun?

❂What is the order of the planets?

❂Does the location of the sun help you predict which planets might be the warmest and which the coolest?

❂Why do you think different sized balls were used for different planets?

❂Which planet is the smallest, and which is the largest?

❂What does this activity show you?

The concept of distance in space is difficult to imagine. This activity assists students in visualizing and constructing a scale model of the solar system. The sun is actually 93 million miles from Earth. In this miniature model it is only 7.5 tissue sheets away. This model shows the planets, their order and their proportional distance from each other and the sun.

Expansion

After students observe and communicate their findings of the tissue galaxy model, instruct them to close their eyes and turn their backs on the model. Teachers can check for keen awareness and observation by quietly changing the order of the ball models on the tissue path. Start simple by exchanging the sun and Earth positions, then gradually switch additional planets. See if students can place them back in the proper order.

Curriculum Connectors

Language /Math/ Social Studies

This activity integrates these subjects through the process skills of: comparing, contrasting, arranging information, sequencing, counting, measuring, and interpreting the chart.

Another way to integrate is to have students write creative sentences using the first letter of each planet in its solar sequential order.

Example:

My Very Energetic Mom Just Served Us Nine Pizzas.

(Mercury, Venus, Earth,   Mars,   Jupiter, Saturn,   Uranus, Neptune, Pluto

Art

Have students draw their vision of a visiting Extraterrestrial being.
✪Do you think your E.T. would be able to adjust and live on Earth?
✪Where did it come from?
✪How would you know?
✪Would it be a predator or a prey? A carnivore or herbivore?
✪How would it get the food it needs?
✪How would it move around?
✪How might its weight on Earth compare with its weight on its home planet?

Role Play

Write the names of the nine planets and the sun on ten strips of paper. Put all the strips in a bucket or container so each student can withdraw one.

First, students must find the person who is holding the sun label and from that person outward, cooperatively organize their solar system model. After the solar system is set up, the planets can begin their movements around the sun.

If you have a very large class, you may need several buckets containing separate solar system paper strips so that several groups can role play at the same time.

Trade Books

The Magic School Bus Lost in the Solar System - Cole
The Planets in our Solar System - Branely
My First Book of Space - Hansen
Space Voyager - Boase

Assessment Tips

One assessment tool which can prove helpful is to propose to students that they draw the solar system on a piece of paper. Tell them the assumption is that they would have to shrink the system in order to fit it on the paper.

Another large group assessment played as a game would be to have the facilitator individually hold up the balls which make up the solar system model and ask the students to identify which planet each might represent. To truly test the students, make certain that additional balls and spheres (oranges, balloons, grapefruit, etc.) which were not part of the original solar system model are employed. Part of the assessment here is to see if students can apply size relationships to different objects.

Piggy Back Poem

Tissue Trek

Nine planets, and one bright sun,
Arranged in a certain pattern,
Just what is the distance, one might ask,
From the sun to Mars or Saturn?

By gathering up a variety of balls,
And a full roll of toilet tissue,
Sizing and sequencing the sun and planets,
Becomes the most interesting issue!

On a scale model solar system,
We can arrange, compare, and measure,
The eight planets that orbit our sun,
Plus Earth, the one we treasure!

lp

DOC To The Moon

Wonder Wise	Have you ever **wondered why** the moon appears in different parts of the sky, and why its shape appears different at different times? You can find secret letters in its phases (DOC).
Topics	Phases of the moon and reflective light
Materials	*Moon Tickets* (Worksheet 1), *Classroom Chart* (Worksheet 2), markers and a sky to observe

Classroom Chart Example:

January						
Sunday	Monday	Tuesday	Wednesday	Thursday	Friday	Saturday
		1	2	3	4	5
6	7	8	9	10	11	12
13	14	15	16	17	18	19
20	21	22	23	24	25	26
27	28	29	30	31		

Discovery Procedure

A Moon Watch can last a couple of months or an entire school year; whichever time frame you use, start with a full moon. Students should observe the moon and report to the teacher/class daily describing what they saw. The teacher will collect the class Moon Tickets and record this data onto a large Classroom Chart to record patterns and changes. Students may make flip books with the collected Moon Tickets.

As students become confident in collecting moon data, assign cooperative groups on each day of the week to collect, record, and report moon observations to the class. (One group will be assigned Monday, another group Tuesday, etc.) The teacher should also be assigned a moon day. Observe and discuss what happens on cloudy nights also. To establish a pattern, the moon must be observed at a specific time each night for a minimum two month cycle.

New Moon	Waxing Crescent *Age: 3-4 days*	First Quarter *Age: 7 days* *Waxing*	Full Moon *Age: 14 days*	Last Quarter *Age: 21 days* *Waning*	Waning Crescent *Age: 24-25 days*	New Moon

Can you find the letters *DOC* in the phases of the moon?

Concept Development

After the previous night's tickets are returned, compare, discuss and decide which moon ticket pattern to transfer to the official class bulletin board display.

✪Do we always see the moon?
✪Is it always in the same spot in the sky?
✪What happens to the moon on cloudy nights?
✪Does it always look the same size and have the same shape?
✪Why do you think we see different shapes?
✪Can we see the moon during the daytime?

Start making daily predictions using *Dial–a–Moon* (Worksheet 3) and the *Moon Moments Chart* (Worksheet 4). Students will learn the correct vocabulary as they continue to observe and record daily data.

Facilitator Facts

The moon appears to wax (grow) in size to a full moon, then wane (shrink) to nothing. This happens because during most of the month, only a portion of the sunlit half of the moon is visible from Earth.

A lunar month is approximately twenty–nine and one half days. A neat way to remember waxing and waning: We *wax* a car to make it shiny, but the shine will go away if it *wanes* (rains).

	Moon Phases/Terms
	NEW: darkened or very dimly lit
(Waxing)	CRESCENT: smaller than half of the moon's face
	FIRST QUARTER: half of the moon's face is visible.
(Waxing)	GIBBOUS: appears larger than a quarter moon yet is not full
	FULL: entire face of the moon is seen
(Waning)	GIBBOUS: appears larger than a quarter
	LAST QUARTER: half of the moon's face is visible
(Waning)	CRESCENT: smaller than half of the moon's face.

60

Expansions

MOON

EARTH →

"MOON STICK"

•*Moon Sticks*: mount a styrofoam ball on a pencil (it represents the moon). Have a student hold it to the light. The student represents Earth and the light represents the sun. As the student holds the ball out with an extended arm, have the student turn slowly in a small, counterclockwise direction. and observe the light as it changes on the ball. (Earth moves counterclockwise as does the moon.)

✪What changes as you watch the moon stick?

✪How does the light change?

✪Can you form a lunar eclipse? (Move the moon to block light from both Earth and sun causing total darkness. Keen observation is required.)

Notes: The shadow on the moon ball appears best inside, using an overhead projector as the sunlight. If you use outside sunlight, warn students about safety to their eyes. *They are not to look directly at the sun!* They should watch only the moon ball and the light on it, not the sun!

•Use a bike reflector and flashlight in a dark room to demonstrate the moon's reflective light.

•Wrap a string around a basketball 10 times. Unwind the string and attach one end to the basketball and one end to a tennis ball. Stretch the string between the two balls; this represents both the approximate size differential between Earth and the moon as well as representing the distance between the two.

Curriculum Connectors

Math

Cut an apple into fractional parts which compare to the moon's phases. The data collection, charting and graphing from moon observations automatically integrates this subject.

Language Arts

Vocabulary and decoding skills:
sh = shadow/shade; **ph** = phases; **oo** = moon; **gh** = light; **a** = wax; **a** = wane.

Explain to students that the moon has influenced literature in books and poetry as well as forming a large part of the world's legends and mythology.

Students should write a story about the moon using their new vocabulary.

Social Studies

Interpretation of the visual charts and graphs of the collected moon tickets connects this activity to social studies.

Art

See *Dial–a–Moon* (Worksheet 3) to add this connection.

Role Play

One student acts out the part of the sun, one the moon, another Earth. Have the students act out the motions of these heavenly bodies through the course of an entire lunar month.
Note: The moon character needs to keep the same face to Earth while orbiting.

Trade Books

Maggie's Moon - Alexander
Papa Get Me The Moon - Karle
Sky Detective - Docekal
Many Moons - Thurber

Assessment Tips

Have students use **Moon Tickets** to name phases. Have them draw the moon's phases in order or place the phases in order using the **Orderly Moon Cards** (Worksheet 5). Ask students to name, label or sequence all the phases in order, beginning with a new moon.

Piggy Back Poem

Moon Moves

While the moon reflects the light of the sun,
Earth glimpses some of the rays.
And brings a cycle of phases
That repeat every 29 days.

A *new* moon seems to be gone from
    the sky,
While the moon's back catches the light.
Then *waxing* begins and
    a crescent appears,
Bringing more
of the moon

Halfway through those 29 days,
The moon is *full* and bright.
It gradually *wanes* away to a sliver,
And ends up being hidden in the night!

Worksheet 1
(DOC To The Moon)
Use for charting, graphing, data collection,
and "flip books."

Moon Watch Tickets

Worksheet 2
(DOC To The Moon)
Enlarge and use for collecting results
of nightly *Moon Tickets.*

Classroom Chart

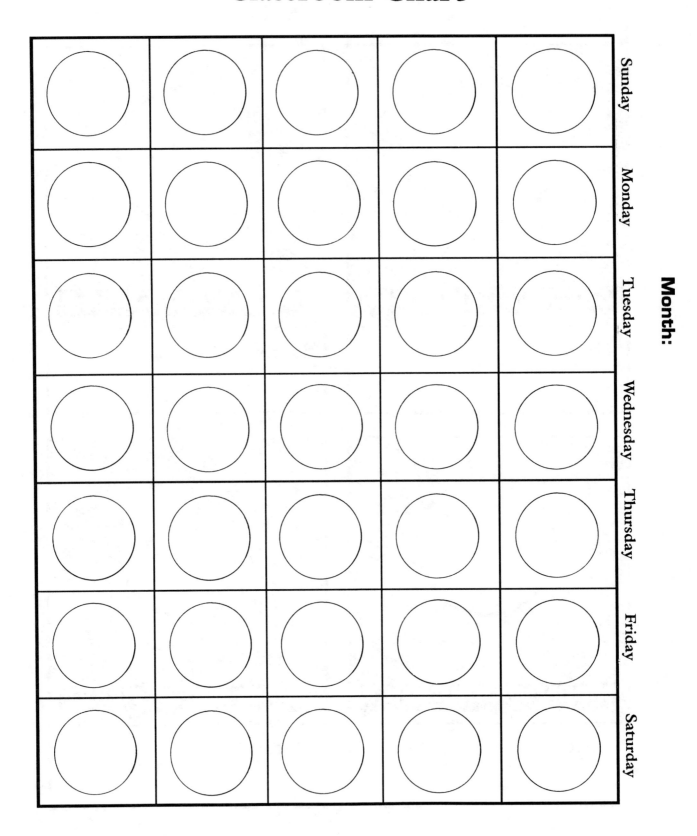

Month:

Sunday · Monday · Tuesday · Wednesday · Thursday · Friday · Saturday

The teacher can use this activity to build moon vocabulary. Make a daily prediction on this moon clock. (This works well as part of a classroom weather station with a daily leader making the prediction for the next day.)

The moon moves counter–clockwise.

✪How does the movement of the hand on the Dial–a–Moon compare with the movement of the hands on the clock in your class room?

Dial–a–Moon
SUN is Here

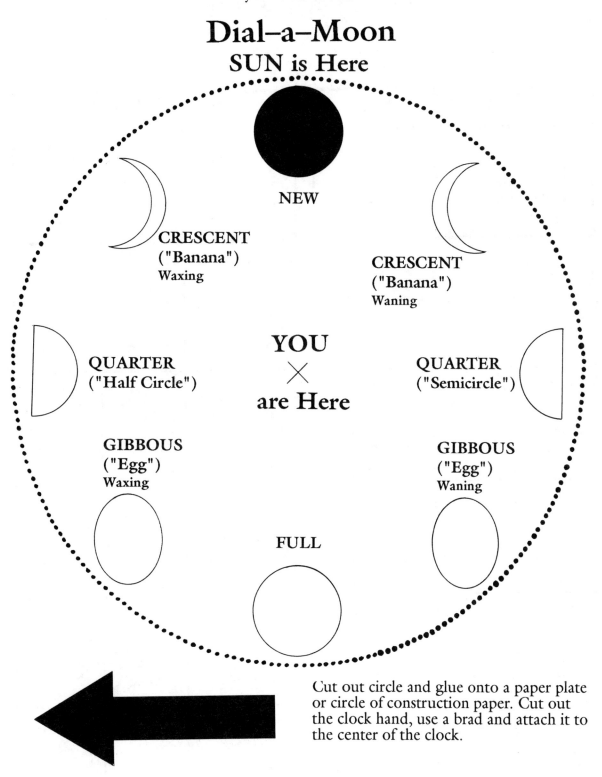

CRESCENT
("Banana")
Waxing

CRESCENT
("Banana")
Waning

NEW

YOU
✕
are Here

QUARTER
("Half Circle")

QUARTER
("Semicircle")

GIBBOUS
("Egg")
Waxing

GIBBOUS
("Egg")
Waning

FULL

Cut out circle and glue onto a paper plate or circle of construction paper. Cut out the clock hand, use a brad and attach it to the center of the clock.

Worksheet 4
(DOC To The Moon)
Use daily to chart and graph.
A date is needed only on the first and
last squares.

Moon Moments

PREDICTION	OBSERVATION
I think it will be_____days until the next *full* moon.	I counted _____days from one *full* moon to the next.

FULL

Date:

Date:

Orderly Moon Cards

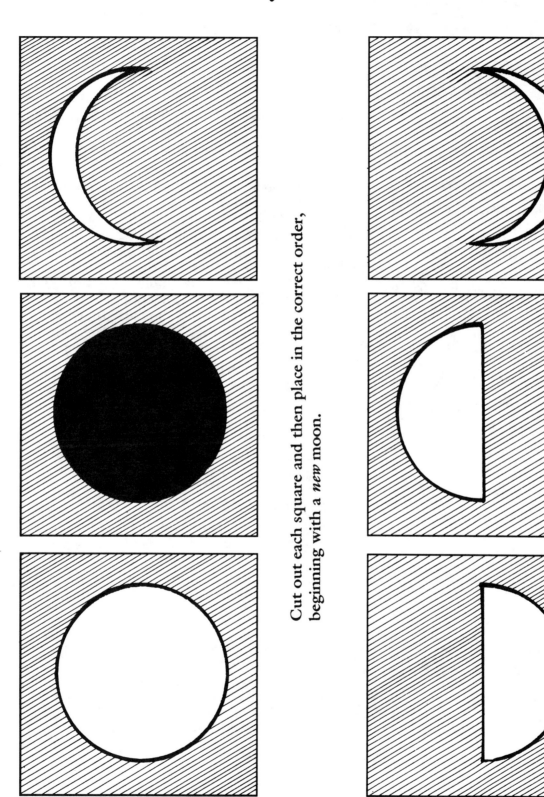

Cut out each square and then place in the correct order, beginning with a *new* moon.

Body Shadows

Wonder Wise

Have you ever **wondered why** your shadow changes size as the time of day changes?

Concepts

Shadows, rotation of Earth, and telling time

Materials

Chalk of various colors and a concrete/paved area or a sidewalk, and of course, a sunny day

Discovery Procedure

Have students line up with their backs to the sun. Ask them to look down and describe what they see (shadow). Students should then select a shadow buddy and let them trace each other's body shadows. Students should always stand in the same spot (chalk an outline around their shoes) as they recheck their shadows at hourly intervals beginning at 9 a.m. Each new shadow will be marked with a different color chalk and labeled with student's initals. Students should place a prediction X on the pavement to indicate where the head of the new shadow will be at the next time interval. Always predict!

11:00

PREDICTION ⟶ X

8:00

Concept Development

✪Why do you think the shadows weren't in the same place?
✪Were your prediction X's close?
✪Why do you think the shadows moved or changed?
✪Does Earth move or does the sun ?
✪When does the earth seem to have a shadow? (night)
✪Can you use the shadow movements to predict other things? (time)
✪In which direction does the shadow move?

68

Facilitator Facts

Earth constantly spins, or rotates, on its axis; we are constantly going from day to night. Use a globe and a flashlight in a darkened room to demonstrate this. From Earth, the sun appears to move across the sky; Earth seems to stand still. Although the sun gives the *appearance* of moving across the sky from east to west, it is actually Earth that is rotating. Shadows change because of Earth's rotation.

How can we experience the idea that it's Earth which moves and not the sun? Have a student sit in a swivel chair and note the position of a particular ceiling light in the room (which represents the sun). As the student in the chair (representing Earth) turns, so does the position of the sun appear to change.

Expansions

Adopt a small outdoor shadow. Draw its outline on white butcher paper recording the date and time. Recheck this shadow every 5-6 weeks to observe seasonal shadows.
✪Do you think there will be any difference? (Earth tilts and revolves around the sun so shadows will experience changes).

Have students face north and see if they can create a human sundial.

Curriculum Connectors

Math

Have students measure the length of their shadows at hourly intervals on their *Shadow Sheet* (Worksheet 1).

Language Arts

Provide students with chalk so they may write descriptive words on their body shadows as they change.

Social Studies

Help students find places on the globe which have day when you have night. Use a dark room with the light from an overhead as the sun.

Art

Let students trace their body shadows on white butcher paper, adding the wardrobe they think will be good for tomorrow's weather.

P.E. Games/Role Play

Organize a game of shadow tag. Shade is the base. If shadow chaser(s) touches your shadow, you're out.

Trade Books

Nothing Sticks Like A Shadow - Tompert
Shadow Chaser - Cosgrove
My Shadow - Stevenson

Assessment Tips

Process evaluation will be evident in observations, self–awareness, verbal, and written communication of shadow changes.

Product evaluation can be collected data from Worksheets 1, and 2.

Piggy Back Poem

Shadow Truths

Sun rise, sun set.
Is that really true?
The sun is actually sitting still,
While E*arth* has a move or two!

Earth turns gently on its axis.
So every single day,
Our shadows move around and about
In a very special way.

dp

Shadow Sheet

A.

Shadow Time	Shadow Length in cm	Shadow Width in cm

B. Label and measure three of your classmates' shadow heights at 10:00

Classmate's Name	Length in Centimeters

C. How do the length of three of your classmates' shadows compare with yours?

_____

_____

_____

_____

A Timely Shadow

Draw a picture of what your shadow might look like at:

Time_____	Time_____
Time_____	**Time_____**

Radical Rotations

Wonder Wise

Have you ever **wondered why** tornados happen and what sets them off?

Concepts

Tornados, twisters, cyclones, funnels, vortexes, weather, thunder clouds, air pressure, equalizing pressure, water pressure, and fluid movement

Materials

Two 2–liter plastic pop bottles, food coloring, three inches of five–eighths inch PVC tubing (this size is the same diameter as the opening of the bottles). If the PVC tubing is not available, grey duct tape will work for a temporary demonstration. If you prefer, commercial *Tornado Tubes* are available from science suppliers and toy stores.

Discovery Procedure

(1) Have students insert the PVC tubing around the neck of one bottle. Fill this bottle with water to the top of the neck.

(2) Students now attach the second, empty bottle into the other end of the PVC tubing. Secure with duct tape.

(3) Have students invert the connected bottles so that the water–filled one is now on top. Water from this bottle will begin to run into the empty one on the bottom.

(4) As the water changes bottles, instruct students to rotate the water–filled bottle in a circular motion. This will cause the water to begin to whirl, forming a funnel–shaped air column in the center.

Students should repeat this rotation phenomenon many times making observations, predictions, and recording data.

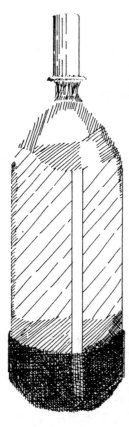

(1)

(2)   (3)   (4)

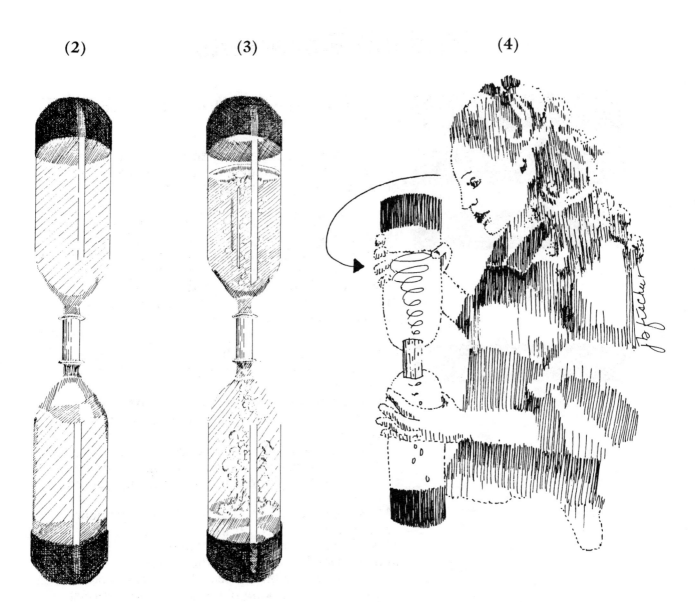

Concept Development

Encourage students to share their observations, predictions, and collected data.
✪Where do you think the motion in the bottle comes from?
✪Did you notice what pulls the water through the opening?
✪In what direction does the water rotate?
✪Is it the same each time?
✪What changes each time? Watch closely.
✪Do you hear anything during the rotation?
✪What does it sound like?
✪Have you ever seen a whirlwind, a tornado or a hurricane?
✪Would it be safe to stand and watch a real one?

74

This radical rotation system permits convenient, repeated and safe observations of whirlwind dust devil/twister/funnel/cyclone/tornado phenomena.

The water represents a cold, polar air mass which is dry and heavy; the air in the bottle represents a warm, moist, gulf air mass.

The first element in a real tornado is a strong thunderstorm that has constant rotating updrafts. This causes a rising stream of low pressure air. The swirling uprush of warm air creates a *tornado vacuum* or low pressure system (much like the action of a household vacuum cleaner). The air draws surrounding air from the ground upward and toward it.

Scientists are still uncertain exactly what sets off these unusual storms.

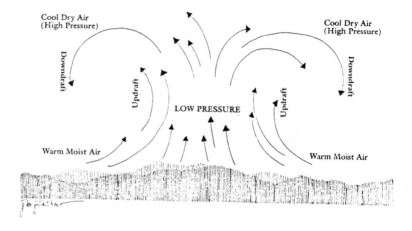

Expansion

Have students add glitter, a small object like a Monopoly® house, a math cubic gram weight, and pieces of toothpick to the water in the bottle. Watch what happens to the glitter (debris) and the objects (houses, barns, buildings, etc.) during a radical rotation. The toothpick pieces show how trees and other wood debris are put into motion during a tornado

Curriculum Connectors

Math

Have students time how fast the liquid storm moves from one container to the next. Encourage them to race with their classmates. Compare the time of the rotation to the time the water takes to just drip without a rotation.
✪What is the time difference? Record your answer.

Encourage students to write a math story problem to describe their findings.

Language Arts

Now is a great time to share the literature and/or the movie of the classical favorite, *The Wizard of Oz* by Frank Baum.

Health & Safety

Practice a classroom tornado drill. Encourage students to discuss the warning systems and signals commonly used in their school and community. Discuss where students should go if they hear a tornado warning if they find themselves:

(1) at the mall;
(2) at home alone;
(3) in a mobile home or automobile.

Note: Go to basements, under stairs or heavy furniture or get into closets in the middle of the house. If you are in a mobile home or car, get out and go to a public shelter or to a neighbor's basement or lie flat in a ditch and cover you head with your hands.

Social Studies & Art

Work with students to draw a map of the United States. Label the Gulf of Mexico and *Tornado Alley*. Some research should be required to locate this alley. You may wish to do this activity on a large classroom map. Find where the warm, moist air mass and the cold, polar air mass originate.

Warm and cold air masses clash above the flat plains area of the U.S. producing violent storms and winds that have earned this area the nickname of "Tornado Alley."

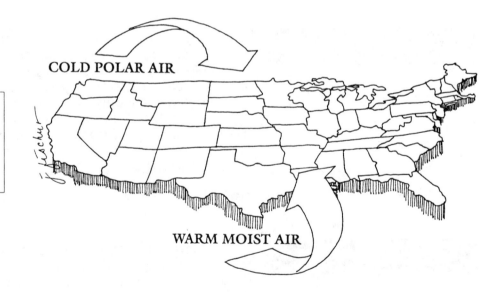

COLD POLAR AIR

WARM MOIST AIR

76

Trade Books

Nights of the Twisters - Ruckman
Summer Storm - Shore
Tornado - Milton
Tornadoes - Armbruster

Assessment Tips

This activity is an assessment of visual literacy and student communication. Questions should be asked of all students to assess their visual understanding of how rotations form, like:
✪What do you think causes the water to move in a tornado motion?

Piggy Back Poem

Storm Forming

It's a twister!
How did it form?
Strong, mighty winds,
Make quite a storm!

Warm, moist air moves in from the Gulf
Meeting cold, heavy air from the North.
The winds and pressure form a storm
Bringing a *Radical Rotation* forth.

A spout may be pulled down to the earth
Linking this turbulent cloud to the ground.
The funnel darkens as it makes its way,
Tossing dirt and debris all around!

Rock & Mineral Candy Comparison

Have you ever **wondered why** there are rocks and minerals, and what they might have in common? Can you tell the difference between the two?

Concepts

Rocks, minerals, and mixtures

Materials

Mini crunch–candy bars (Sample One), Mini plain chocolate candy bars (Sample Two), hand lens, white paper, and *Rock or Mineral Comparison* (Worksheet 1).

Discovery Procedure

Using *Rock or Mineral Comparison* (Worksheet 1):

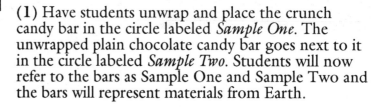

(1) Have students unwrap and place the crunch candy bar in the circle labeled *Sample One*. The unwrapped plain chocolate candy bar goes next to it in the circle labeled *Sample Two*. Students will now refer to the bars as Sample One and Sample Two and the bars will represent materials from Earth.

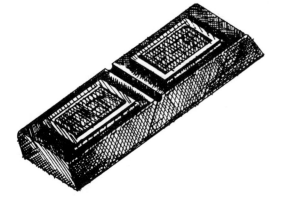

(2) Students need to observe these samples closely (touch, smell, sight, but not taste yet). Students should investigate the samples from all sides and angles. In the space above the questions, have students draw each sample, making certain they draw all the details they observe.

(3) Explain to students that when scientists work with an unknown material it is important to observe all parts of the material. Have students carefully break Sample One in half. They can eat one half but must save the other half for observation. Students are to answer question two under their drawing.

Students should now break Sample Two in half, eating one half and observing the other. Again, have students answer question two beneath their drawing. The facilitator is looking for ways the two samples are alike and how they are different.

Concept Development

Referring to question one on the worksheet, have students observe Sample One answering whether it appears to be made of one substance or more than one. Have them record their answer. Have students answer the same question for Sample Two. Again they need to record their answer.

✪How can you relate your observations to substances we find on Earth?

Facilitator Facts

Sample One and Sample Two are used as models for comparing rocks and minerals.

Minerals are made of only one substance each found naturally in Earth. They include such common substances as salt, the graphite used in pencil leads, and talc in powder. They also include rare finds such as silver, gold, and diamonds. Minerals are similar to the plain chocolate bar because they are solid, uniform in chemical composition, and appear to have the same crystal structure throughout. Minerals also appear never to have been part of a living organism.

Rocks, on the other hand, may be either composed of only one substance, or be a mixture of different minerals. Granite, for example, is formed mainly of the minerals quartz and feldspar. Some types of rocks are made up of the remains of living organisms. For example, coal is a solid mass of fossilized plant material. Rocks are more readily found than are minerals. Rocks, like the crunch candy bar, appear to be composed of more than one ingredient. The crunch part of the candy bar could be compared to different materials forming the rock, or even to the remains of living things such as land plants or marine animals like corals and clams.

Expansion

Take students on an outside field trip, and have them collect a variety of rocks. See if they can find their own Sample One and Sample Two.

Use chalk on a sidewalk/pavement to make a large sorting chart, and have students place their rock samples in the appropriate sample section.

Trade Books

Sylvester and The Magic Pebble - Steig
Eyewitness Book: Rocks and Minerals - Symes
Everybody Needs a Rock - Baylor
Ming Lo Moves the Mountain - Lobel

Assessment Tips

For your students, write the words Mineral and Rock on the board. Ask students to write or invent their own questions which use only those two words for answers. Have students observe what additional words seem to consistently appear in these questions.

Piggy Back Poem

Rocky Rhymes

Minerals, we find, are solid and smooth,
Made up of non–living things.
The rare ones, like silver and gold,
Might end up as bracelets and rings!

Rocks are a mixture of minerals,
And maybe things once living.
A variety of rocky formations,
To us, the earth is giving!

dp

Rock or Mineral Comparison

Crunch Candy Bar

SAMPLE ONE

Drawing Box

(1) How many substances does Sample One look like it is made from? _____

(2) Explain how Sample One and Sample Two are alike and different.

ALIKE

DIFFERENT

Plain Candy Bar

SAMPLE TWO

Drawing Box

(1) How many substances does Sample Two look like it is made from? _____

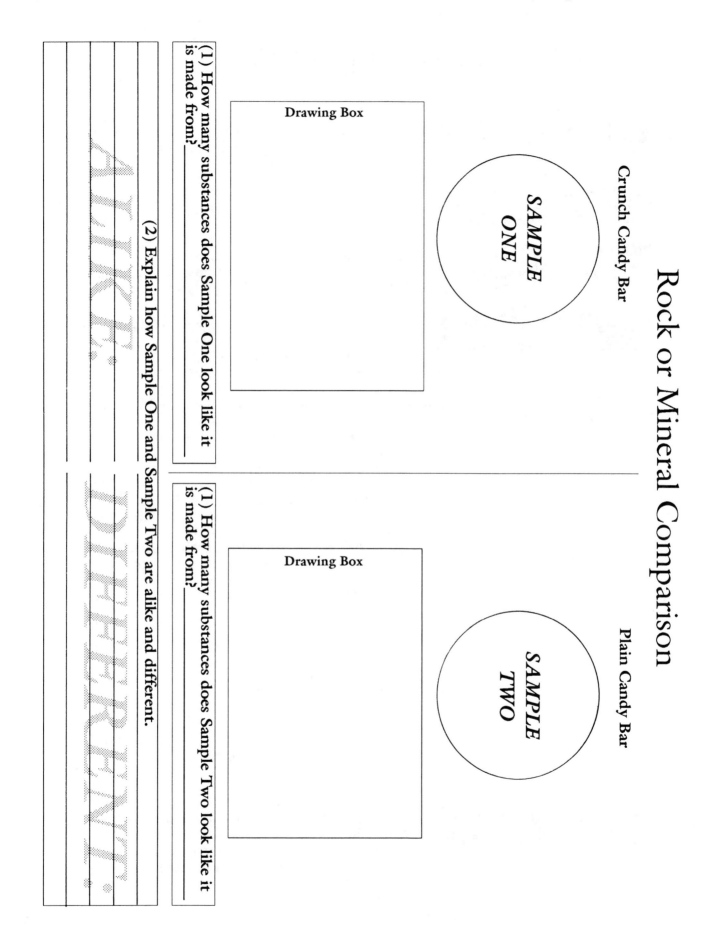

Retrieving Rocks

Wonder Wise

Rocks all seem so very different. Have you ever **wondered why** geologists place some of them in similar families? How do scientists test each rock to find out the rock's identity?

Concepts

Geologists, rocks, texture, luster, shape, weight, search, sort, and classification

Materials

Outdoor rocky area, containers or tub of water, paper towels, egg cartons, magnifying lenses, and an equal arm balance or other scale

Discovery Procedure

The best way to start this rock exploration is to read *Everybody Needs a Rock*, by Baylor.

If you do not have access to this book, then dig into discovery. Go outside to rocky areas, giving each student or group an egg carton to hold twelve different rock samples. Each rock must fit in the egg holder slot; rock samples should not be larger than an egg. *Check List* (Worksheet 1) may be used on this outdoor rock expedition.

After returning from the rock hunt, students will need to wash the dirt from their rocks and look at them with a magnifying lens. They will have to look at their rocks very closely to see the hidden history they hold.

Next, have the students sort their rocks in as many ways as they can. Guide students to consider properties such as size, shape, color, texture, shine (luster), and weight, but accept any reasonable suggestions.

The rocks can also be sequenced from:
- largest to smallest
- lightest to darkest
- roughest to smoothest
- longest to shortest
- shiniest to dullest.
- Ask students to think of additional ways to sequence the rocks.

Concept Development

✪What words (adjectives) can you think of that describe your rocks?
✪What do all these rocks have in common?
✪What differences do you see in the rocks?
✪Do you think rocks have a continuous life cycle?

Facilitator Facts

Most people think all rocks are rigid. However, some are smooth and easy to bend and crumble with your hands. Students may also define rocks as heavy sinkers. But, if you drop a huge piece of pumice stone into water, it will float!

Geologists define rocks as substances made up of one or more minerals. Rocks are exposed as a result of wind, water, and ice continually wearing away layers of sediments. Rocks change and new formations occur with each volcanic eruption and plate movement under the earth's surface. By studying rocks and how they recycle, scientists can learn more about Earth and the changes which have occurred over time. That is why it is important to look a rock *right in the eye* and learn about its family make–up and its past generations.

Expansions

Communicate to students that they will be experimenting with their rocks using some basic geological tests:

It may be best to set up these rock test stations in centers around the room so students can rotate in small groups. Monitor closely for safety.

(1) THE STREAK TEST

The streak test reveals the *true colors* of rocks. Have students stroke each of their rocks on the back of a household ceramic tile or on a concrete sidewalk. They should group together those rocks that leave the same color streaks. It may be necessary to form a group of rocks that leave no streaks. Explain that the true color of a rock may be superficially changed by environmental factors, and the results from the streak test indicate the rock's true color. If a streak is not made during the test, this indicates that the rock being tested is harder than the tile or concrete.

(2) THE HARDNESS TEST

This test demonstrates how *hard* a rock is. Students will use fingernails, a penny, table knife/steel fingernail file, and a babyfood jar or soda bottle to learn the hardness of each rock.

Have students work through the following stages of testing to check the rock for its hardness. Using *Rigid Rocks* (Worksheet 2) and the following categories, chart all findings:

a. A **very soft** rock can be scratched by a fingernail.
b. A **soft** rock can be scratched by a penny, but not by a fingernail.
c. A **medium** rock will scratch a penny, but will not scratch a table knife/steel file.
d. A **hard** rock will scratch a table knife/steel file, but will not scratch glass.
e. A **very hard** rock will scratch glass.

(3) THE ACID TEST

Use this test for *chemical reaction* to group rocks in yet another way. Have students place a few drops of vinegar on each rock. They are to group together those rocks that react to the vinegar; and group those that do not. Rocks that contain the mineral carbonate (such as limestone and marble) will cause the vinegar to bubble or fizz.

Curriculum Connectors

Math

Ask students to answer some simple math story problems relating to the collected information. For example, if there are 20 students in our class, and only three students could find a shiny rock, how many students did *not* find a shiny rock?
(20 – 3 = 17 students)

Ruler of Rocks (Worksheet 3) provides a pattern for a rock ruler. Instruct students in the use of this ruler outdoors to measure the smallest sand granules to progressively larger pebbles, cobbles, and boulders.

Language Arts/ Social Studies/Art

Ask students to select a favorite rock from the egg carton collection.
✪If you place it in a group with many other rocks, could you still find it? Have students try it.

Now they should name their rocks and listen to this problem:

Pretend your rock is your own little planet. Look at the rock closely.
✪Where would you build your house?
✪Did you pick a high spot or a low one?
✪Where would you plant your garden?
✪Why would you need one?
Find a place on your rock planet to dig a water well.
✪What other things would you *need* on your new rock planet?
✪What additional things would you *want* on your planet?

Instruct students to draw a picture of their new rock planet. Make certain they draw and map all the areas discussed in the problem.

Social Studies

Invite a guest speaker from the library, nature center or museum to discuss your particular geographic area. A local geologist will have information about rock and mineral sites to explore in your locale.

Encourage students to look for rocks in mountainous areas, volcanic regions, outcrops, beaches, river banks, stream beds, road cuts, and cliff bases.
✪What kind of rocks could you expect to find in these areas?

Trade Books

When You Find a Rock - Klaits
Everybody Needs a Rock - Baylor
*Magic School Bus Goes to the
        Center of the Earth* - Cole
Sylvester and the Magic Pebble - Steig
Eyewitness Book: Rocks and Minerals - Symes

Assessment Tips

Teacher observation is a key assessment tool in the early discovery stage of this activity (sorting, classifying). The student worksheets and recorded data will assess student growth and understanding of rock observations and classification.

A performance assessment may also be used to evaluate understanding. Example:
- Sort your rocks in families by size, shape, color, and texture.
- Sequence the rocks from darkest to lightest using the streak test.
- Place the rocks in order from hardest to softest.

Piggy Back Poem   *Rocky Road*

It's a *rocky* road we travel,
On our way from here to there.
Let's take some time to study a few,
Since rocks are everywhere.

Look those rocks *right in the eye,*
Take notice of each one.
Smooth or rough, shiny or dull,
Classifying can be fun!

Are they heavy or light, crumbly or hard?
Compare, sort, and measure.
Discovering all the differences,
Makes the study of rocks a pleasure!

Check List

A Find a rock that is:

☐ the size of a mouse.

☐ round.

☐ square.

☐ the size of an apple seed.

☐ smooth.

B Look for a rock that will:

☐ crumble if you rub it in your hand.

☐ jump in your pocket when you run. (Try it!)

☐ sparkle in the sunlight. (What colors do you see?)

C ☐ Look for five rocks that will fit in your hand at the same time.

D ☐ Dip one rock in water. Did it change? How?

E ☐ Find one rock to smell. What did it smell like?

F ☐ Touch your favorite rock 100 times. What happened?

G ☐ See if you can find a sinker–rock and a floater–rock.

Pick out six of your favorite rocks, test them, and place them in the appropriate columns.
✪Did you have more of one kind of rock than other kinds?

Rigid Rocks

Very Soft	Soft	Medium	Hard	Very Hard

Ruler of Rocks

Join and Tape here

COBBLE

PEBBLE

GRANULE

SAND

Bottom of Ruler

Directions:

Cut out both pieces of the ruler. Overlap them where marked to form one long ruler which will measure the smallest grains of sand on the bottom, to fairly large boulders at the top.

Example:

By placing the example rock at the bottom of the ruler, one can see that it falls into the PEBBLE space, thus designating it as a pebble–sized rock.

BOULDER

COBBLE

PEBBLE

GRANULE

SAND

Top of Ruler

BOULDER

COBBLE
(Continued)

Join and Tape here

Cookie Expedition

Wonder Wise

Have you ever **wondered why** people find dinosaur bones in the ground and who puts those bones back together again? Have you ever wondered how a scientist can tell which head or tail belonged to which animal? Who are these people and how do they know where all the pieces go?

Concepts

Paleontologists, fossils, and digging tools

Materials

Cookies (M&M® cookie, and one sample of shaped cookies such as: sugar, butter, or animal), napkins or tissues, toothpicks, small plastic bags, and magnifying lenses

Discovery Procedure

In advance, break each sugar, animal, or butter cookie into five to seven pieces and place in a plastic bag. You need only one of these kinds of cookies. (The M&M® cookie will be used later in the expansion activity.) Be careful not to mash the pieces as you break the cookie.

Distribute a bag with a broken cookie to each student or cooperative group. Tell students to place contents of the bag on the napkin, and encourage them to try to arrange the broken pieces into the original cookie shape.

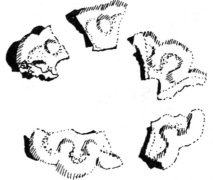

Concept Development

✪What shapes did you construct?
✪Were some shapes more difficult than others?
✪What if you had no idea of the original shape of the cookie?
✪Would it be easy to confuse some parts?
✪Could the results vary?
✪What clues did you use to put your cookie fossil together?
✪How might this method compare with the work paleontologists do in reconstructing fossils?

Paleontologists are fossil detectives. They try to solve mysteries by discovering clues and interpreting them correctly. Paleontologists puzzle out the mysteries of the past. They try to put the fossil puzzles together to find clues about past plants and animals. Fossils embedded in successive layers of rocks are like printing on the pages of a book from the past. They tell the story of ever changing life.

Expansion

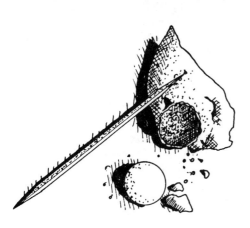

Discuss the work of paleontologists emphasizing that much patience and a variety of tools are necessary for paleontologists to do their job. Photographs of tools and paleontologists at work can be helpful. Students should understand that the paleontologist's work consists not only of the physical act of safely recovering the fossils, but also includes surmising the original shape of the fossil, its function, and the possible reason for its death or destruction.

Give one hard M&M® cookie to each student and have them remove the M&Ms® (now fossils) from the surrounding cookie dough sediments using only their fingers.

The cookie represents the limestone that often surrounds the fossil a paleontologist is examining in the field. The object is to do as little damage as possible to the fossil while extracting it from the surrounding rock in which it's embedded. The fossils need to be preserved for closer studies in the lab.
✪What are the advantages/disadvantages of digging for fossils using your fingers as your only tools?

Now give students a second cookie and have them repeat the activity. This time they are to use the toothpick as a tool to help them pull the M&M® fossils away. The magnifying glass or lens is essential for careful extraction.
✪Are the results the same in the experiments with Cookie One and Cookie Two?
✪Why/why not?
✪How did the tools help you?
✪Can you find another way to carefully remove the M&Ms®?
✪What did you see happening to the surrounding cookie parts when you used only your fingers?
✪How much more time do you think it took using the toothpick tool?
✪Which do you think is more important in the careful removal of an unknown fossil, saving time or preserving the fossil in good shape? Give reasons for your answer.

Curriculum Connectors

Math/Art

The cookie was somewhat easy for the student paleontologists to reassemble. Would it be so easy to put the pieces together if their cookie was as big as a dinosaur? Just how large is a dinosaur? Have students try this activity to find out.

Take students outside and have them draw, measure, and compare a life sized dinosaur sidewalk chalk drawing to themselves. Metric measurements for one of the most popular dinosaurs, the *Tyrannosaurus Rex*, are as follows:

Length 13m	Height 6m
Head 1.2 m	Jaws 90 cm
Talons 20 cm	Arms 76 cm

Language Arts

Encourage students to write a creative story using a *what if* situation. Children like these open–ended story lines, because they allow their imaginations to soar with limitless possibilities:

What if your house pet were a dinosaur?
What if dinosaurs were still alive today?
What if you found a baby dinosaur on
　　your doorstep?
What if you met a dinosaur in a dark alley?

Social Studies

Explain that the history of life on earth is divided into three main eras:
　Paleozoic - the age of ancient life
　Mesozoic - the age of dinosaurs
　Cenozoic - the age of mammals

Scientists estimate the earth's age to be near 4,600 million years old. Help students interpret this concept of time by explaining that if a student lived a millions *days* they would be 2,740 years old!

An enrichment activity could include the designing, charting, and making of a classroom time line.

Music/P.E./Role Play

Students can move to music the way they think different dinosaurs might have moved. The teacher may call on students to name a dinosaur to imitate.

Trade Books

Dinosaurs in Your Backyard - Mannetti
Danny and the Dinosaur - Hoff
Digging up Dinosaurs - Brandenberg
Draw 50 Dinosaurs and Other Prehistoric Animals - Ames

Assessment Tips

This assessment may be written or oral:
• Describe the job of a paleontologist.
• Explain what information fossils give us.
• Name some of the tools you think you would need as a paleontologist.
Performance assessment involves solving the cookie fossil puzzle.

Piggy Back Poem

Fascinating Fossils

The study of ancient life,
PALEONTOLOGY, as it is known,
Involves fossils of plants and animals,
A diary of the past in stone.

Patience and care are the keys,
In safely removing a *find*.
The drilling, and chipping, and chiseling,
Must always be gentle and kind.

The parts are brushed and cleaned,
Packed and transported with care,
Then grouped, studied, and labeled,
And assembled for all to share!

dp

Cracker Quakes

Wonder Wise

Have you ever **wondered why** the ground beneath your feet seems so solid and unmoving? Does it really ever move?

Concepts

Faults, moving geographic plates, and earthquakes

Materials

One can of chocolate frosting, one graham cracker per student, plastic knives or craft sticks (for spreading frosting), and waxed paper

Discovery Procedure

Have students place a piece of waxed paper on their desks. On it, each student should place two graham cracker halves side by side (sides must be touching). Next, using a knife/craft stick, have students spread a spoonful of frosting over the top portion of both crackers (crackers should still be touching each other). Students should, very slowly slide one cracker forward while holding the other in its original position. They must observe very closely to see what happens.

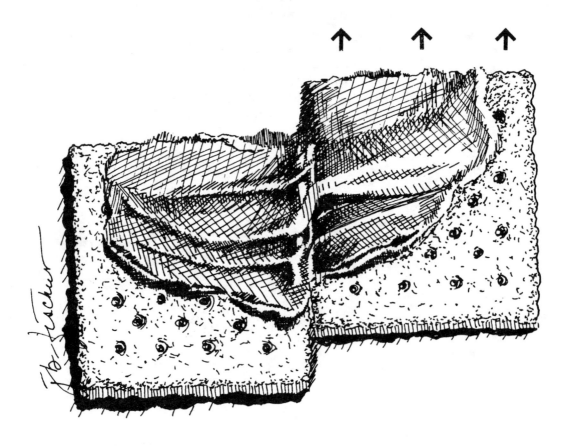

94

Concept Development

✪ What happened to the frosting as the cracker moved?

✪ What happens if you move the two halves slightly sideways and away from each other?

✪ Can you relate these movements to how the earth moves beneath us?

   The cracker represents the crust of the earth.

✪ What does the chocolate frosting represent? (soil)

✪ Did the crust's movement disturb the soil in any way?

✪ What would be a good name for the crack lines? (faults)

Facilitator Facts

   This activity demonstrates how the earth's surface moves beneath us. Earth's outer crust is not one solid piece like the shell of an egg. The soil (chocolate frosting) was changed as the rocky plates (crackers) slowly moved past each other. If the plates move away from one another they form a fault line. Most earthquakes result from the movement of crustal plates as demonstrated in the cracker quake. In reality, Earth rarely ever opens apart from itself. It usually slides, shifts, or overlaps one part on top of another. The solid ground beneath our feet (the rock which forms Earth's crust) is not as stable as it seems.

Expansion

   Now have students push the crackers one on top of the other. Observe what happens.

✪ What do you see forming? (mountains and hills)

✪ What motion do you see in the soil frosting?

Now you can eat your cracker plates and frosting soil!

Curriculum Connectors

Social Studies/Art

Have students locate the state of California on a map. California has earned worldwide attention for its earthquake happenings. Explain that the San Andreas Fault is a gigantic boundary between two of Earth's great, shifting crustal plates. The fault is nearly 700 miles long, and extends from the Gulf of California in the south, to that part of the Pacific Ocean north of San Francisco. Encourage discussion and have students draw and label their findings.

Introduce the American seismologist, Charles Richter, who devised a numerical scale for rating the strength of earthquakes. An earthquake rated 2 on the Richter Scale releases ten times as much energy as a quake rated 1 on the scale. Structural damage is unlikely unless an earthquake rates a 5 or more.

Language Arts/Safety

Encourage the writing of creative stories or drawings of a new earthquake invention by your students. Their invention or idea should detect and warn people about earthquakes *before* they happen. This invention/plan should include a safe place for people to go. Brainstorming this topic first with the entire class would be helpful.

Role Play

Move outside and have students form two lines facing each other. Tell them each line represents a plate on opposite sides of the San Andreas Fault in California. Have one child join hands with a person opposite him/her and explain that they now represent a highway which crosses the fault line. On a teacher signal, the two lines should take ten steps sideways in opposite directions. The highway should break apart during the shift. When plates shift, fences, bridges, highways, and buildings are broken apart. Explain that this is the kind of shifting which occurs during extensive earthquakes like those in San Francisco.
Be careful – students are like earthquakes; they can be unpredictable. Close supervision is required.

Trade Books

Mountains and Earth Movement - Blain
Our Violent Earth - National Geographic Society

Assessment Tips

Have students write a brief paragraph or draw a picture explaining the causes of earthquakes. Make sure they explain how an earthquake might effect highways and houses.

Piggy Back Poem

Faulty Footing

That good, old, solid ground,
Lying beneath our feet,
Covers a series of *plates*,
Shifting where they meet.

When that continual shifting,
Gets a little too frisky,
Faults are sometimes created,
Making things a little risky!

Sudden movement along a fault,
Can cause the earth to quake,
Leaving surface changes,
In its mighty wake.

dp

Rain, Rain, Come Again Another Day

Wonder Wise

Have you ever noticed a puddle of water on the sidewalk? Do you ever **wonder why** puddles go away so quickly? Where do they go?

Concepts

Water cycle, evaporation, condensation, precipitation, accumulation, and water vapor

Materials

Quart size resealable bags, small clear medicine cups, masking tape, a sunny window, and water

Discovery Procedure

(1) Instruct students to tape a resealable bag at an angle (like a diamond) on the glass of a warm, sunny window. Slanting the baggie will allow the water droplets to slide down and collect in the bottom corner of the bag.

(2) Next, each student should fill a medicine cup one–third full of water. They need to mark the water line with a permanent marker, then gently tape the cup inside the bag's lower corner (see illustration below). Finally students should seal their bag.

(3) For the next seven to ten days have students observe their bag daily and record changes in their *Water Log Journal* (Worksheet 1).

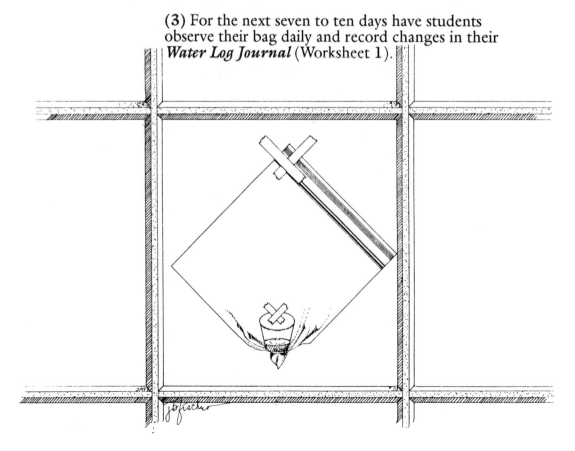

Concept Development

✪ Does the water in the medicine cup invisibly evaporate?
✪ How is it like oceans, lakes, ponds, and puddles?
✪ What is forming inside the bag?
✪ Where are the "clouds" in your bag?
✪ When it "rains" in the bag, where does the accumulation go?
✪ Where is the ground level in your bag?
✪ What happened to the marked water level on the cup?

Discuss the natural water cycle stressing the processes of evaporation, condensation, precipitation, and accumulation. Have students put together the *Rain Puzzle* (Worksheet 3). Discuss with students that they have created a simple, mini–water cycle in a closed bag system. Relate the various steps of the water cycle in the mini baggie system to the bigger, natural water cycle on Earth.

Facilitator Facts

The sun is the power that keeps the water cycle in motion. It warms the surface of the sea, changing water into vapor. Water also evaporates from glaciers, lakes, and streams. More water is added by all leafy plants through the process of *transpiration*. In the air, this invisible vapor condenses and forms the billions of droplets and ice crystals that make up the clouds. Eventually the moisture in the clouds returns to earth as rain, snow, and other forms of precipitation. It then evaporates once again, continuing its never–ending cycle.

Expansions

Have students pour a small bucket of water on the pavement and draw a white chalk line around the perimeter of the puddle. They should check their puddle every five or ten minutes. Make sure they draw an outline around each new puddle. Soon the puddle will be very small or totally gone.
✪ Where has all the water gone?

Have students do the same experiment again but this time with salt water. This is a method of *desalination*, which is separating salt from water by evaporation.
✪ What is left behind after the water is gone?

For an enrichment activity, students can design a self–watering plant container (terrarium) based on the mini water cycle bag system.

Curriculum Connectors

Math

Have students measure the number of milli-liters of water that evaporated from the medicine cup in the bagged water cycle. Have them compare their measurements with their classmates'.

Write math problems on the board with a small wet sponge. Students must try to solve the problems before they vanish.

Language Arts/Art

Guide students through this learning cycle posing questions that will lead them to identify and build vocabulary: clouds, precipitation, accumulation, ocean, lake, ground water, etc.

Read *Cloudy with a Chance of Meatballs* by Barrett. Have students write their own creative story based on this book and title it *Cloudy with a Chance of_____*. Students can then design a cloud mobile to match the story they wrote.

Cloudy With A Chance of Planets

MERCURY

VENUS

EARTH

MARS

JUPITER

SATURN

URANUS

NEPTUNE

PLUTO

Cloudy With A Chance of Candy

Role Play

Have students role play a recycling rain drop by having them start in a standing position falling from a cloud. Next have them curl up in a puddle and when the sun comes out (designate a student to be the sun) the students stand and vaporize back into the air, then condense to form a cloud before precipitating back to the ground. Let the students help you design additional parts to reenact the water cycle.

Trade Books

A River Ran Wild - Cherry
Where Does Water Come From? - Vance
The Magic School Bus at the Waterworks - Cole
Cloudy with a Chance of Meatballs - Barrett

Assessment Tips

The *Water Log* Journal (Worksheet 1) can be used to assess observations and understanding.

A product assessment may be used if students draw and/or label the parts of the water cycle using *Water Cycle* (Worksheet 2).

Piggy Back Poem/Music*

Circulation Regulation

The sun is the power in EVAPORATION,
Sending vapor in the air to form CONDENSATION,
Which in time falls down as PRECIPITATION,
Gathering here and there in ACCUMULATION,
Once again ready for EVAPORATION,
A cycle in no danger of TERMINATION,
Keeping water on Earth for the whole DURATION,
Which is glorious news for life and VEGETATION!

lp

* See if students can set this poem to Rap music using their own style and rhythm.

Draw pictures of daily changes. Write observations below each drawing.

Water Log

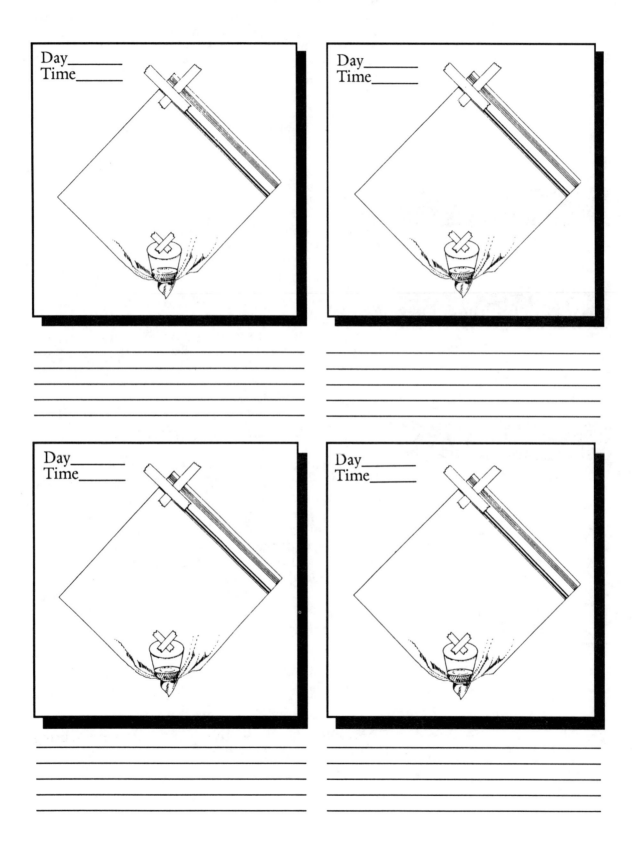

Day_____
Time_____

Day_____
Time_____

Day_____
Time_____

Day_____
Time_____

Water Cycle

(1)_____   (4)_____

(2)_____   (5)_____

(3)_____

Rain Puzzle

WATER ACCUMULATION

CONDENSATION

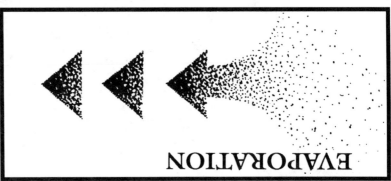

EVAPORATION

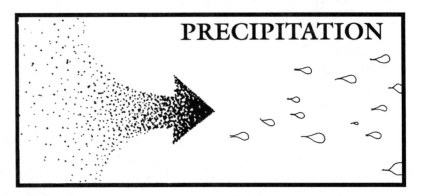

PRECIPITATION

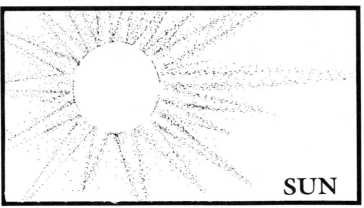

SUN

Recycled Big Books

Wonder Wise

Have you ever **wondered why** garbage causes so many problems? What can we do to help solve this problem?

Concepts

Environmental awareness, recycling, reusing and landfills

Materials

Brown paper grocery sacks, scissors, glue, various art supplies to illustrate recycled book

Discovery Procedure

Have students cut up the side of the grocery sacks, then carefully cut the rectangular bottom off. Next, flatten two sacks out and glue the printed sides together; it will take 2 sacks to make two pages with a front and back side.

Encourage students to set up a recycling center in a classroom, corner or other designated area. Students can go to the center to cut, color, and paste in free time. It will take some time to build up a class supply of recycled big book pages. Students and parents may wish to do a few pages at home to speed up the process.

This is a great activity to take into other classrooms for mentor teaching and storytelling. These recycled pages also serve as the makings for wonderful science logs and journals.

While the page–making process is underway, brainstorm with students concerning the subject matter their big books will contain. Students should first submit a rough draft of a story, and next create preliminary illustrations and cover design ideas to go with their story.

The finished story, illustrations, and cover design will appear on their recycled big book. Encourage students to cut, fold, and in other ways adapt the big book pages to work with their individual story idea. Let imaginations run wild. See samples on following page.

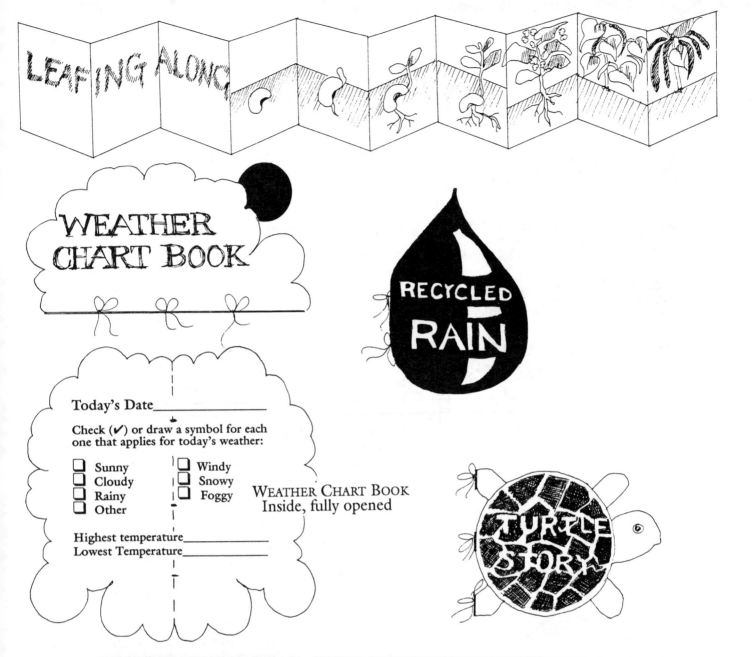

LEAFING ALONG

WEATHER CHART BOOK

RECYCLED RAIN

Today's Date_____

Check (✔) or draw a symbol for each one that applies for today's weather:

☐ Sunny ☐ Windy
☐ Cloudy ☐ Snowy
☐ Rainy ☐ Foggy
☐ Other

Highest temperature_____
Lowest Temperature_____

WEATHER CHART BOOK
Inside, fully opened

TURTLE STORY

Concept Development

✪What does the word recycle mean?
✪Why do you think it is important to recycle and reuse?
✪What kinds of trash could be recycled?
✪What are you doing at home to recycle and reuse?
✪What is your community doing to recycle?
✪What is your school doing to recycle?
✪Can you think of ways we waste materials and create excessive trash?
✪What are some ways we could cut down on this everyday waste?
✪How do companies package their products?
✪Do you think they could cut down on their packaging?
✪Have you heard about any companies that are trying to improve on excessive packaging?
✪Why do you think they are attempting to change?

106

Students in your class are taking an active role to preserve their environment by recycling and reusing. This is a primary step to creating awareness in young people that recycling and reusing begins in their own backyard. Students are making useful classroom supplies out of sacks that would have otherwise found their way to a landfill.

A landfill is a place for trash, where each layer of garbage is packed down then covered with soil.

Recycling, or reusing trash, is a better solution. More than half of our trash could be recycled if more people took the time. Aluminum and tin cans, glass, plastics, and paper can now be turned into new products and used again.

Although often thought of as interchangeable, recycling and reusing are not one and the same. Recycling means trash must be processed in order to regain use. Reusing requires no reprocessing, just finding a new use for a previously used item. Discuss these terms with your students. Are you making Recycled bag books or Reused bag books?

Expansion

Give each student a cleaned milk carton saved from their school lunch. Also give them a wooden craft stick, some glue, a ping–pong sized ball of modeling clay, and one sheet of paper from the scrap pile. Students can now each design and construct a small sail boat to use in a contest.

Outdoors, have students set up large containers of water or a small wading pool on which to test their recycled sail boat inventions. Encourage students to remake sails and adjust their designs if they think a better model might be more successful. Students can race these inventions from one end of the container/pool to the opposite side. Wind, durability, engineering, and problem solving are prime factors for a winning boat.

Curriculum Connectors

Math

Help students to graph these facts:
Americans throw out in one year;
•238 kg (524 lbs.) of paper
•104 kg (229 lbs) of yard waste
•50 kg (111 lbs.) of metal
•48 kg (105 lbs.) of glass
•46 kg (101 lbs.) of food waste
•38 kg (83 lbs.) of plastic
•56 kg (124 lbs.) of miscellaneous items
✪How much total weight of trash do Americans discard every year? (580 kg or 1,277 lbs.)

Discuss how people in the United States throw out about three and one–half pounds, or 1.5 kg of trash every day! That means the whole country produces about 868 million pounds (394 million kg) of trash daily. This would fill 63,000 garbage trucks!

Landfills are big, and it takes about 20 years to fill one. Scientists predict that at this rate, by the year 2010 only one out of four landfills will still be open; all the rest will have been filled to capacity!

Language Arts/Art

Having students construct, write, and illustrate a big book story is a strong integration of this subject.

Art

Take a walk with your students and pick up and collect trash. Back in the classroom, have students select pieces of the collected trash to sculpt, compile, and glue into different kinds of creative art.

Encourage students to disguise their original materials so well that it is difficult to identify the piece of art was made from recycled material.
Make sure students wash any garbage before they begin handling it for the project. Instruct students to always wash their hands with soap and water after handling trash or any unknown objects. Use of disposable gloves are recommended.

Experts say on a one–mile walk, an average of 1,457 pieces of litter will be found.
✪Do you think this is an accurate statement?
✪How many pieces of litter did you find?

Social Studies

Inform students that Americans are using creative problem solving to help Mother Earth with her trash crisis.

Florida changes trash into compost. Compost is a mixture of rotted kitchen garbage and soil which is used as a garden fertilizer. Shredded kitchen waste is mixed with a special enzyme and stored in a large pile where it heats up and breaks down into a rich soil full of nutrients. It is highly valued by gardeners and farmers alike.

Michael Reynolds, an architect in Taos, New Mexico is helping people construct houses using old tires and aluminum cans. These recycled objects are the building blocks of his construction method.

In Austin, Texas, the city chops up about 34 million Christmas trees every year and turns them into wood chip mulch for gardeners.

California crushes old toilets and uses them to make shiny gravel to pave roads. This sparkling pavement makes it easier for drivers to see at night.

During the 1920s in America, pigs were used to "pig out" on trash. Nearly half the U.S cities used pigs to get rid of food waste. (The trade book *Big Science Garbage* by Scholastic will enhance this discussion.)

Trade Books

Big Science Garbage - Scholastic
Come Back, Salmon - Cone
My River - Halpern
Recycle! A Handbook for Kids - Gibbons
A River Ran Wild - Cherry

Assessment Tips

The recycled big books, boats, and art projects may serve as written and communicative assessment tools.

The active, creative problem solving of reusing the recycling materials will be evident in the actual products.

Application assessments will occur if you observe students improving and not being wasteful of school and campus materials.

Parent comments on recycling also provide a valuable assessment. Many students newly aware of helping the environment will recycle, reuse, and minister to their family.

Piggy Back Poem

Treasure That Trash

We throw away too much.
Our landfills are quickly filling.
To change all that we merely need,
To be ready, able, and willing!

It begins at home, recycling does,
With everyday things we use.
Like glass, aluminum, plastic, and paper,
Those things we **can** reuse!

Before we head out to the trash,
Let's look at what we've got.
It doesn't take long to recycle,
And to Earth, it means a lot!

Life Science

Pumpkin Probing

Wonder Wise	Have you ever **wondered why** pumpkins look the way they do and what might be inside them?
Concepts	Pumpkins or gourds, autumn season and plants; shape, color, sinking, floating, and estimation
Materials	Small pumpkins or gourds (washed and cleaned to remove all toxic sprays), paper towels, knife, water, large container and blindfolds (If gourds or pumpkins cannot be found, use apples.)
Discovery Procedure	Give each group of students a clean, washed pumpkin. Before having students probe the inside of their pumpkin, have them observe the following basics concerning the exterior. Have students observe the pumpkin carefully using all senses *(**EXCEPT TASTE**– some pumpkins are treated with toxic sprays)* and record their findings on their *Pumpkin Observations* (Worksheet 1). Tell them to not forget to knock on the pumpkin. Take the group of pumpkins and mix them together. See if each group can find their pumpkin. Blindfold group members and have them use their sense of touch to find their pumpkin from among the others. Next, sequence the pumpkins lightest to heaviest based on group predictions. Finally, weigh the pumpkins on a scale to check these predictions.

113

Concept Development

Discuss the observations each group collected.

✪How did your observations help your group identify your pumpkin?

✪How are the pumpkins the same and how are they different?

✪Did the size make a difference in the actual weight of the pumpkins?

Hand each pumpkin back to the group and do teacher–guided observations with questions such as these:

✪Can you tell which side of the pumpkin was on the ground when it was growing?

✪When you knock on the pumpkin, where is the sound the lowest and highest?

Observe the stems and describe their shape, color, texture, and length.

✪Are there more creases on bigger pumpkins?

✪Where are the creases the deepest, most shallow, closest together, and farthest apart?

✪From your observations would you say a pumpkin is a vegetable or a fruit? (fruit) What information helped you reach your decision?

Facilitator Facts

Pumpkins are a large and diverse group of plants belonging to the squash family. The fruits are grown in a variety of sizes, shapes, and colors. Many pumpkins are raised as ornamentals while the hard shells of others are grown for very practical purposes such as musical instruments or bowls. Some pumpkin varieties have fibrous interiors which, when dried, can be used like a sponge for scrubbing and cleaning. Pumpkins are edible and have roots and seeds rich in starch and oil.

Expansion

Now is the time to investigate internally: Give each group two pumpkins. Have students predict what they will see when they open the pumpkin by doing two drawings of the cut pumpkin. Where do the students think the seeds will be in the horizontally cut pumpkin and where in the longitudinally cut one? Have them draw their predictions. Encourage students to make the drawing larger than real life as this encourages closer examination, possibly even with a lens or microscope. Give each group two pumpkins that have been precut – one horizontally and one vertically. Next to their prediction drawings, have the students draw the actual arrangement of seeds in each pumpkin.

✪Are the seeds connected?

✪What is the stringy stuff?

✪Is it attached directly to the shell wall?

✪Are the seeds arranged in certain groups or patterns?

✪Is the seed pattern arrangement the same for both the horizontally and vertically cut pumpkins?

Estimate the number of seeds inside the pumpkin, then count them.

Compare seeds and findings to those of the other groups.

✪Are all the findings the same?

Look at the shells.

✪Where are they the thinnest/thickest?

✪Are the pumpkins full or empty?

✪What part of a pumpkin do you eat?

Curriculum Connectors

Math

Basic math concepts and terms: counting, numbers, sense, estimation, data analysis, circumference, diameter, and height

Circumference:
Have students design a "belt" with paper or string that will wrap around the fattest part of the pumpkin. Then lay the paper/string belt along a meter stick to find the distance around the pumpkin.

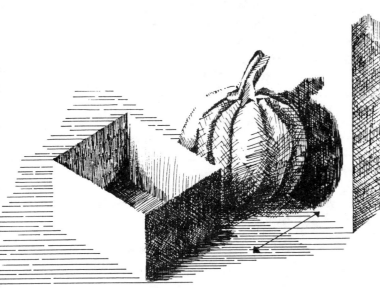

Diameter:
Have students place the pumpkin against a wall and push a box against the opposite side so that the wall and the box look like bookends. They should make sure the side of the box is parallel to the wall. Now, measure. The distance between the two flat surfaces is the diameter.

Height:
Students should lay a flat piece of cardboard over the top of the pumpkin and measure the distance to the floor from the highest part of the pumpkin. That is the height of the pumpkin.

Numerals:
Have students predict and then count the longitudinal lines going around the pumpkin from its "north pole"(stem) to its "south pole" (bottom). Mark the first line counted.
✪Will there be an odd or an even number of lines?
Have students extract the seeds, wash them, and then allow them to dry.
✪How many seeds did the pumpkin have?
✪Where were the seeds located?
✪Were they easy to remove?

Language Arts

• Keep journals of the progress of pumpkin seeds planted by the class.

• Discuss the rhyme *Peter, Peter Pumpkin–eater.*

• Discuss the use of the pumpkin in the fairy tale, *Cinderella.*

• Tell stories using starters like:
  ✪What would you do with an 800–pound pumpkin?
  ✪Would a pumpkin make a good pet? Why or why not? What would you name it?

Social Studies

History of Pumpkins:
Pumpkins were one of the first crops in America. The Indians raised pumpkins long before the white settlers came. Indians used the pumpkin as a food staple; they dried it, ground it into flour, boiled it, and baked it. The Indians cut pumpkin rings and dried them for winter eating. The first pumpkin pies were made in New England by cutting off the top of the pumpkin, taking out the seeds and filling the inside with milk and spices. Maple syrup and honey were added as the whole pumpkin cooked. See if you can find out additional historical pumpkin facts.

Art

Paint pumpkin seeds, attach yarn legs and glue to a large black paper web to hold an assemblage of pumpkin seed spiders.

Paint the pumpkins to look like characters in your favorite book/story.

Nutrition

Baked Pumpkin Seeds:
Place seeds on paper and allow to air dry for at least two days. Have students wash their hands then spread seeds on cookie sheets and bake in a 350° oven for 10–15 minutes until the seeds start popping off the cookie sheet and turn a golden brown. Allow to cool, then peel and eat.

Trade Books

The Pumpkin Patch - King
Pumpkin, Pumpkin - Titherington
The Vanishing Pumpkin - Johnston
The Biggest Pumpkin Ever - Kroll

Assessment Tips

The processing of this activity is in the power of the product. Students can observe, measure, and communicate their findings. The worksheet may be used to collect data and give a written evaluation. Perhaps the next time your students sit at the dinner table they will see their food with new eyes. Maybe they will wonder how many seeds are in a grape, or the thickness of an eggshell. This is critical thinking that will grow to be a part of a child's daily observations.

Piggy Back Poem

Pumpkin Possibilities

Weigh it, measure it, touch it, thump it.
Roll it, taste it, cook it, bump it.

Tough and wrinkled and in many sizes,
Cut "stem to stern," it's full of surprises.

Scoop out the middle and count the seeds.
So much can be used to meet many needs.

What is this fruit, so misunderstood?
A PUMPKIN! It's never looked so good!

dp

Pumpkin Observations

	WEIGHT	CIRCUMFERENCE	NUMBER OF LINES	FLOAT or SINK?
1				
2				
3				
4				

Seedy Sidewalks

Wonder Wise

Have you ever **wondered why** grass grows in the cracks of sidewalks or in other unusual places?

Concepts

Plants, seeds, soil, sunlight, precipitation, and germination

Materials

Outside grassy area, clear plastic containers, lima bean or other bean seeds, potting soil, water, *Seed Journal* (Worksheet 1)

Discovery Procedure

Take a walk outside and look for things growing in cracks, sidewalks, and other strange places. Have students collect seeds, roots, stems, and flowering parts of plants.

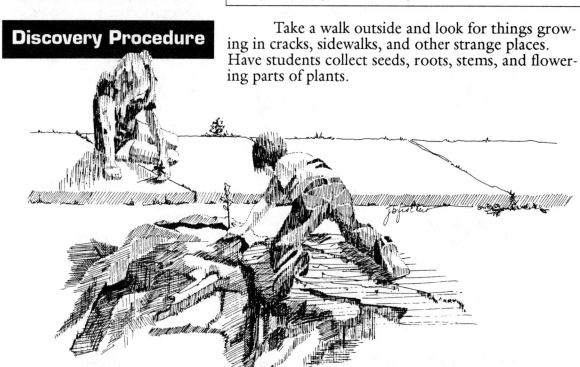

Concept Development

Have students discuss their findings. Discuss what conditions must be in place for a seed or plant to grow.

✪Why do you think you found plants growing in the cracks of sidewalks or in other unusual places?
✪Are the cracks man–made or were some made by the plants as they grew and needed more room?
✪Why do you think plants grow in lakes, oceans, and aquariums?
✪If plants grow so easily in all kinds of places, why do you think we have to work so hard in our gardens and in keeping houseplants alive?
✪What enables a small seed to grow into a tall tree?

Have students sort the seeds, roots, stems, and flowers they gathered, placing them on a labeled classroom chart. This sorting will automatically assess student understanding of plant part identification.

Example: Plant Part Chart

FLOWERS	SEEDS	STEMS	ROOTS

Set this up on the floor using a different color butcher paper for each category.

Facilitator Facts

All seeds require oxygen, water, and a proper temperature to germinate and grow. Oxygen and moisture, initially taken in through the seed coat, and later by the root, help the seed get energy from its stored food supply. Different types of seeds have specific temperature, water, and light requirements. If a sidewalk crack has enough fertile soil, proper temperature, light, and enough moisture, seeds may sprout, and plants may flourish.

Expansion

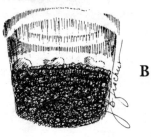

A

B

Students will fill two, clear plastic containers half-full of potting soil. Next, they will plant three lima bean seeds in one container (A). Water until moist. In the other container (B), they will also place three lima bean seeds, but they should lay the beans on **top of the soil**. Mix a small amount of plaster of Paris (make it runny). Have students pour enough of this plaster mixture on the soil in container (B) to make sure they cover the three lima beans which were left on top of the soil. Water both containers every day. Students should make predictions about what they think will happen to the seeds in each container. ✪How do you think the plaster will affect the growth of the seeds in the second container; will it smother the seeds?
✪Are sprouting seeds very delicate, or powerful? Students should record their information daily and compare their findings in the *Seed Journal* (Worksheet 1).

Curriculum Connectors

Math, Language Arts, Social Studies, Art

The journal project and a measurement chart will integrate all these subjects. These combined skills will be reflected in charting, data collecting, measuring, and descriptive notes.

P.E. Games/Role Play

Students can act out the growth of a seed from planting through sprouting, branching out, etc. For example, students lay on the floor in a tight ball, remaining still. A selected Rain Student sprays mist to demonstrate precipitation. Another selected student holds a flash light, turning it on and off to represent day and night. After a few flashlight days have passed, Seed Students will begin to slowly uncurl, standing up and branching out spreading arms and legs to imitate sequential seed growth.

Assessment Tips

Student understanding can be surveyed by the teacher during the Concept Development as plant parts are sorted and charted, and during the P.E. Games/Role Play of the sequential growth of a seed.

Written evaluations can be taken from *Seed Journal* (Worksheet 1).

Trade Books

The Carrot Seed - Krauss
The City Kid's Field Guide - Herberman
From Seed to Plant - Gibbons
Science Book of Things That Grow - Ardley

Piggy Back Song

Seedy Sidewalks
(Sing to the tune of *Silver Bells*)

Seedy sidewalks; weedy sidewalks,
Dressed in seeds, weeds and grass.
In the air there's a feeling of springtime.

Roots are growing,
Tops are showing,
Stretching mile after mile.
And on every cracked sidewalk you'll see:

Sprouting seeds,
Tops of weeds,
Germinating time in the city.

Give them warmth,
Sun and rain
They'll thrive without any pain!

Name_____

Seed Journal

DATE	TIME	DRAWINGS		NOTES
Example: Oct. 24	9:45 a.m.	Plain (A)	Plaster (B)	Seeds in cup **A** are sprouting and curling to top. I can't see anything new happening to seeds in cup **B**.
		(A)	(B)	
		(A)	(B)	
		(A)	(B)	
		(A)	(B)	
		(A)	(B)	

Tators Are Tubers

| **Wonder Wise** | Have you ever **wondered why** potatoes have eyes? Why don't potatoes have seeds? How can you grow more of this nutritional food? |

| **Concepts** | Potato, plant growth, underground stem, and tubers |

| **Materials** | Potting soil, a few potatoes, water, knife, and containers for planting potatoes |

| **Discovery Procedure** | •Give each student a sample of cut up potato (leave skin on and make certain each sample has at least one eye) and ask them to identify it.
✪How does it feel, smell and look? |

•Hand out a two to four–cup container holding potting soil to each student or group. Instruct students to plant the identified potato in the soil burying it at least two inches below the surface. Place the pots on a windowsill and water. Have students predict what will happen to their planted potato. Have them watch for daily changes communicating and recording their findings.

Concept Development

✪Why did you place the potted potato on the windowsill? (sunlight)
✪What else did we need to give to the plant to enable it to grow? (water)
✪How often do you think we need to give the potato water? (every two to three days)
✪Did you predict the potato would grow?
✪Why do you think it grew?
✪How is this potato different from plants you have grown from seeds?
✪What other plants grow this way? (peanuts, Jerusalem artichokes, sweet potatoes and yams)

Facilitator Facts

In a few days you will see evidence of plant growth. How can this be? The eyes, rather than the seeds of the fruit, are planted to grow new crops of potatoes. Potatoes are tubers; a type of underground stem that acts as a food storage organ. Tubers do not contain embryonic leaves and flowers as bulbs do. The surface of a potato has eyes that are actually buds. New potato plants are reproduced by planting pieces of the tubers that contain these eyes. This is how farmers plant their new potato crop.

Expansion

Place a potato in the learning center of your classroom. As the days go by students should observe and record what happens to the potato and its eyes. Have students predict what they think will happen to the potato after days of sitting.
✪What do you think will happen if it sits for months at a time?

Students can also insert toothpicks evenly around the circumference of a potato and suspend it in a small glass of water. Students must make sure they keep the eye(s) of the potato above the surface of the water. Observe the growth.
Have students experiment in the same way with sweet potatoes, planting them both in potting soil and suspending them above water. Have students compare the soil growth to the water growth.
✪Should you expect the same exact results?

Students could also make a comparison study using seed producing plants. Have students place various seeds in a resealable bag with a moist paper towel. In a few days there will be evidence of sprouting. Encourage students to take the seeds out of the bags and compare them with the tuber's growth in both the soil and water.

Curriculum Connectors

Math/Social Studies

Explain to the class that the potato is the fourth most produced crop in the world, surpassed only by wheat, rice, and corn. In the United States the annual per–person consumption is 19 kg (42 lb.) of fresh potatoes and 13 kg (30 lb.) of processed potato foods.

✪How many kilograms or pounds of potatoes does your family eat each year?

✪What is the difference between fresh and processed potatoes? What would be examples of each kind?

The potato plant is native to the Peruvian Andes of South America. Have students find Peru on the classroom map. The potato plant was cultivated in Peru and Bolivia, and along with maize was a staple food of the ancient Inca Indians.

In the mid–18th century, the potato was first planted in Europe and became an important food crop of England and the British Isles. It became a staple food crop in Ireland. When a disease destroyed the crop in 1845 – 1847, over one million Irish people died from hunger.

Art

Instruct each student to bring a potato from home. Have them use the potato shape as the face for a person. Students can add hair, a nose, mouth, eyes, hats, etc. After the potato people are complete, set them aside in an undisturbed place and watch them as they age.

Trade Books

More Potatoes! - Selsam
Mrs. McGingy and the Bizarre Plant - Bishop
Some Plants have Funny Names - Cross
The Hidden Magic Seed - Shuttlesworth

Have students draw a picture of a potato and how it grows. Make sure they label the parts of the plant they have learned.

Piggy Back Poem

Tator Taught

Farmer Icabod from Idaho,
Was teaching his son to plant tators.
"Son," he said, "Listen close,
'Cuz it's nothing like planting tomators!

It's all in the *eyes*, my boy.
These are the special buds,
From which *tubers* grow underground,
Into some mighty fine tasting spuds!"

dp

Germ Raiders & Tators

Wonder Wise

Have you ever **wondered why** you catch a cold or the flu? Can you give these germs to others?

Concepts

Hygiene, cleanliness, mold, germs, and microorganisms

Materials

Small jars or resealable bags, and a few peeled potatoes cut into pieces for each child

Discovery Procedure

Have students divide into two groups: the *Dirty Hands Team,* and the *Clean Hands Team.* To begin, all students need to get their hands dirty. They can rub their hands gently on the ground, floor, or in grass, sand, and soil. Have the Clean Hands Team thoroughly wash their hands with soap and warm water and then dry. Now give each student a potato sample to rub in their hands. They will then put these potato samples into their own jars or resealable bags and seal tightly. Students should label the jars with their names and observe the changes which occur over the next few days.
Do not forget to have the Dirty Hands Team wash their hands after the potato rub!

Remind students to check their project daily, recording the days, times, and changes they observe. Now is a great time to integrate language arts by encouraging students to write, record, and draw pictures of the observed potato changes. Have students compare the differences between the Clean Hands potatoes and Dirty Hands potatoes in their journals.

Concept Development

✪What do you see forming on the potatoes of the Dirty Hands Team?
✪How do the two groups' potatoes compare?
    Discuss how germs on the potatoes might correlate to the germs that moved from the students' hands.
✪Which group of potatoes grew mold first?
✪Why do you think the Clean Hands Team's potatoes eventually grew mold despite their clean hands?
✪What can this experiment tell us about spreading germs and the importance of cleanliness?

Facilitator Facts

    The potatoes of the Dirty Hands Team will grow a colored mold at a rapid rate. The Clean Hands Team's potatoes will eventually start to form the same moldy substance due to germs in the air; even in washing, not all germs are eliminated. The Dirty Hands potato specimens show how germs and microorganisms are invisible but leave evidence of their existence. The Clean Hands Team delayed the growth of these organisms but could not eliminate them entirely. Organisms which you cannot see live on the skin. Some of these moved from the clean hands to the potatoes.

    As the mold cultures continue to grow, they will fill the jar/baggie with strange, unpleasant looking shapes, smells and color combinations.

    Help your students compare the mold in the jars with the experience of being sick; assure them that the mold in their jars is not the same kind that causes illness (unless the moldy potato were eaten)! The cultures in the jars, however, visually represent something which cannot be seen by the naked eye namely, viruses and bacteria of such infectious diseases as colds, mumps, chick pox, and flu.

Expansion

    Encourage students to list some helpful hints they could give to others to keep them from spreading harmful germs or organisms. Maybe someday they will grow up to be doctors. Students should see from this experiment one important preventative health rule to follow – keep your hands clean by washing with soap and water.

    Help students pay better attention to cleanliness, sanitation, and avoiding cross–contamination from one person to another. Remind and discuss with students that prevention is a more efficient way of dealing with infectious diseases than treating the diseases once they've appeared. Nutrition and immunizations are also important.
✪Why do you think you are required to have immunizations before you can come to school?

128

Curriculum Connectors

| **Math/Brainstorm** | Ask students:
✪If you caught a cold and gave it to two people, and *they* gave it to two people, how many people would then be infected?
✪What do you think would happen if this cycle continued without treatment?
✪How many people might this affect if left untreated? |

| **Language Arts/Art** | Having students use their journals in the Discovery Procedure of this activity integrates the subject in written, pictorial, and descriptive responses. Correct punctuation, spelling, and grammar should be used in all written responses.
　Students may wish to design a journal/log with a unique design and follow their own format and organization of data. |

| **Health** | Ask students:
✪How does this activity help you make good, healthy choices for infectious disease protection and illness prevention? |

| **Social Studies** | Explain that infectious diseases have strongly influenced the course of history on Earth. Plagues have changed entire social structures. The outcomes of military conflicts have been profoundly influenced by outbreaks of diseases such as dysentery. Infectious diseases have intruded into human settlements and affected their development.
✪What do you think the term *germ warfare* means? |

Trade Books

Germs Make Me Sick - Crowell
No Measles, No Mumps for Me - *Crowell*
Why I Cough, Sneeze, Shiver,
        Hiccup and Yawn - Berger
Slim Goodbody - Burnstein

Assessment Tips

An application assessment will follow as you hopefully observe more students washing their hands and paying closer attention to cleanliness.

Verbal communication will occur the next time a student forgets to cover a cough or sneeze.

Piggy Back Poem

Getting a Jump on Germs

Germs are found in lots of places,
In coughs and sneezes, on hands and faces.

The way to keep an infection from blooming,
Is to practice plenty of daily grooming.

Cover your nose and mouth with tissue,
So spreading germs won't be an issue.

Wash your hands and face each day,
To keep those nasty germs away!
                                        dp

Odor Decoder

Discovery Procedure

This is a game of pairs. You need one film can per student, with another matching smell container. Make sure you have different smells for each pair.

Each student will need a film can containing a piece of cotton saturated with a safe odor such as: vinegar, steak sauce, perfume, kitchen spices, liquid smoke, etc. Students will have a match to another class member. The teacher will need to mark cans with matching numerals/letters and make a record of which odor is in each can.

Students should be advised on the safe smelling method called *wafting*. **Wafting is done by gently pulling air and smell toward your nose with a fanning motion of your hand.**
✪Why is this method used?
✪When would you sniff? (Never an unknown substance)

Students will now roam the room trying to decode their odor and match their scent to classmates'. The students should not show or reveal codes until they think they have correctly identified their matching smell. Students may not talk among themselves; they must use only their sense of smell to locate the matching odor person. Repeat procedure until correct odors are found by all students.

Concept Development

Ask students if their odor reminds them of a particular occasion or situation? Now see if they can match the smell to the teacher key.

✪Why do you think animals use their sense of smell?

✪Do you think their sense of smell is stronger than humans'?

✪If an animal gets separated from its group, how can it find its way back?

✪Could you smell your way back home?

✪Would it be easy to use your sense of smell to find your way home?

Facilitator Facts

Animals use their sense of smell to find food, mates, family, and territories. Bees, ants, wasps, and termites use *pheromones*, scented secretions, to direct or alarm others. Humans smell by means of a nerve in our upper nose which leads directly into the brain. Our sense of taste is also based on our sense of smell. Humans' sense of smell does not appear as strong as the sense of smell animals possess.

Expansion

Sort and chart the odor cans by:

SWEET	ROTTEN	STINKY

Have students find other smells in the classroom or on the playground to add to the class collection.

✪Can you add some additional describing words on your chart?

Curriculum Connectors

Math

Discuss pairs.

✪What is a pair?

✪How many are in a pair?

✪What were the pairs in this game?

List things that come in a pair.

Language Arts

Assist students in writing a poem about what smell tells us.

132

Social Studies

As a class, go outside and observe ants marching from one spot to the next. **Do not disturb them.**

✪ How do you think an ant uses its sense of smell?

✪ How might it help them survive or find their way to their colony?

See if students can map out the route to the ant colony.

Art

Use scented markers to draw a picture. Use only **one** color (black = licorice; red = cherry, etc). Hang pictures at nose level, and have the students close their eyes and see if they can guess the color of the picture.

Trade Books

Sight; Hearing; Touch; Smell; Taste - Series by Ruise
Look Again - Hoban
*The Secret Language: Pheromones in the
        Animal World* - Johnson
Sense Sensation - Aliki

Assessment Tips

Have students write a brief paragraph about how the sense of smell helps people and animals in their protection and survival.

✪How did it help you in this game?

Piggy Back Poem

Sniff and Go

Smells, smells everywhere,
On land and sea and in the air.
I find if I sniff and taste as I go,
I can identify *what* and *who* I need to know,
And find the things that are right for me.
Taking me just where I need to be!

djw

Worm Wonderment

Wonder Wise

Have you ever watched a robin try to pull a worm out of the ground? Do you ever **wonder why** it is such a tug–of–war? Just what anchors those little worms into the ground?

Concepts

Earthworms, segments, bristles, anchoring, and decomposition

Materials

Waxed paper, paper towels, magnifying lenses, soil, disposable aluminum pans, paper, pencil, ruler, digging tools, and earthworms

Discovery Procedure

It is best to take students outside and let them dig for their own earthworms. Students can also collect a soil sample at the same time. *Students will need to wear a plastic glove to protect them from harmful microscopic animals which may be in the soil.*

Before you begin, have students put the earthworm in water for a few seconds to clean it. Observation skills will increase if students can clearly see the worm's body.

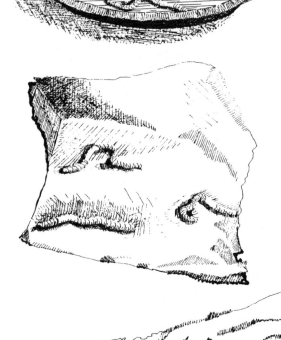

• Have students place their earthworms carefully in the disposable pans. They should observe the worms with magnifiers and discuss their findings.

• Students should then move their earthworms to waxed paper for 4–5 minutes and communicate their findings and observations.

• Next, have students move the earthworms to a damp paper towel for 4–5 minutes and discuss what they observe.

• Finally, have students carefully place the worms on soil samples for 4–5 minutes and observe how the worms react.

Concept Development

✪What surface did the worm prefer?
✪Do you see or feel bristles on the worm?
✪How does the worm look and feel?
✪Do you see little circles or segments on the worm's body?
✪Can you tell if the worm has a head and tail? (anterior/posterior)
✪What observations helped you decide which end is which?
✪How did you come to your conclusion?
✪Do you notice any other unusual markings?
✪Are these markings helpful?
✪What type of creature is an earthworm? (Invertebrate – animal without a backbone)

Facilitator Facts

One creature vital to decomposition and recycling of organic materials is the earthworm. The worm's constant mixing of the upper layers of soil allows air and water to percolate through the soil improving its quality for living plants. Earthworms have mouths, but no teeth. The narrow, pointed end which thickens to force soil apart is the front end of the worm. Everything earthworms eat is pushed through their digestive tract and small, pellet–like piles emerge. These castings are a valuable plant fertilizer.

The most noticeable features of an earthworm's anatomy are the rings or segments along the length of its body. Each segment is surrounded by a set of muscles connected to adjoining segments by another set of muscles. This allows the worms to lengthen, contract, move, and twist through the soil. The tiny bristles (setae) on each of the body segments help the earthworm both move and anchor itself. This is why a bird works so hard to pull the earthworm out of its burrow.

Worms are invertebrates, animals without a backbone. Other examples of invertebrates are: insects, clams, crabs, jellyfish, lobsters, octopus, shrimp, snails, squid, starfish, sea anemones, spiders, and parasites.

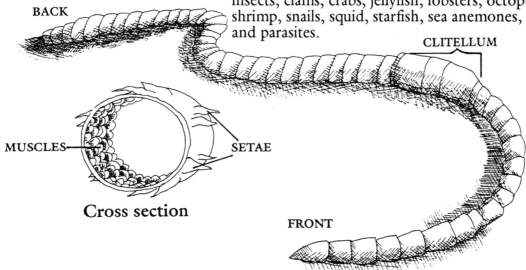

BACK

CLITELLUM

MUSCLES

SETAE

Cross section

FRONT

135

Expansion

This discovery stage will test the earthworm's sensitivity to its environment. Direct students to put the worm back in the aluminum pan, and experiment in the following ways:

•Shine a flashlight at the worm.
✪How does it respond?
✪Does it need this response in its natural environment?
✪Have you ever seen worms dried up or dead on the sidewalk?

•Cover the flashlight with red plastic wrap or red tissue paper. Now shine it on the earthworm.
✪How does the worm respond now?
✪How does this compare to how the worm responded to the bright light?

•Lightly tap on the pan edges with a pencil to cause vibration of the pan.
✪How does the worm seem to respond to the vibrations?
✪How might this help the worm in its underground environment?

•Put worm in the soil container, water heavily, and observe the worm's reaction to the rain shower.
✪How do you think this reaction helps them survive?
✪Do you think earthworms can drown?
✪Have you ever noticed earthworms in water puddles?

Curriculum Connectors

Math

Have students predict the length of their earthworm in centimeters.
✪How could you measure this creature most accurately?
Remember, these invertibrates shrink and grow as they contract the muscles in their segments. Have students measure the worm when stretched out and when shortened. Assist students in drawing a bar graph estimating and comparing the worm's actual measured length. Stress that students should be as accurate as possible. (Using a string to measure the worm, and then measuring the string with a ruler seems to work best.)

Have students dig up a small volume of soil from their school playground. Have them predict the number of worms they will find in this soil sample. *Again, be sure students wear a plastic glove to protect them from harmful microscopic animals which may be in the soil sample.* Have students carefully extract the worms from their sample and count them. From this information, have students estimate how many worms they could expect to find in the whole playground area.

Language Arts

Have students construct and and then write a recycled big book on worm facts. (See Recycled Big Book unit, page 105, for directions.)

Help students write a creative story about an earthworm giving advice to a farmer.

Social Studies/Math

Assist students in building an earthworm maze constructed on a surface of moist paper towels and waxed paper using cardboard barricades to form the path of the maze. Small tiles collected from hardware stores also make good maze walls. Put leaves and soil at the end of the maze as an attraction for the worm.

Before placing the worm at the beginning of the maze, have students predict how long it will take the earthworm to complete the mapped out path.

When the earthworm is in place, have students time the worm to track its actual travel time to the end of the maze.

✪Do you think the worm will learn the path?
✪After several trips down the path will the worm decrease the time it takes to reach the end of the maze?

Have students chart their findings.

P.E. Games/Role Play

Instruct students to act out the movements of an earthworm. Students will lay on the floor and try to lengthen by stretching, and shorten by contracting their muscles. Using these movements, have students attempt to move across the floor of the room.

✪Do your muscles work like those of an earthworm?
✪Was it easy to move across the floor?
✪How could you anchor yourself if a big robin decided to have you for lunch?

Trade Books

How to Eat Fried Worms - Rockwell
A Worm's Tale - Lindgren
Andy and the Wild Worm - Thayer
It's Easy to Have a Worm Visit You - O'Hagan

Assessment Tips

Direct students to list all the facts they know about earthworms. Ask the students to list questions they still have about earthworms. Verbally quiz students on how they could decide to experiment or test to find some answers to these questions. Allow students to interview classmates, asking questions about what they learned and how they now feel about worms after experimenting and taking a closer look at them.

Students can also interview parents. This encourages student communication and helps them connect the home and school experiences in the learning process.

Piggy Back Poem

Crafty Crawler

I have to admit, I'm quite a worm.
And that's a big surprise,
Since the job I do doesn't require,
Any teeth, or ears, or eyes!

My segments, muscles, and bristles,
All help me move through the soil,
Where I recycle organic matter,
As I contract, twist, and toil.

So go ahead and pick me up,
And take a good long look.
Then put me gently back on the ground,
And not on a fisherman's hook!

dp

138

Recycled Rainforest

Wonder Wise

Two hundred years ago, 20 percent of Earth's land was covered with rainforests. In 1994 that figure has dropped to approximately 3–7 percent. Do you ever wonder why this devastation is occurring? Why should we be concerned? Can we build it back?

Concepts

Rainforest, deforestation, global awareness

Materials

Used brown grocery bags, scrap paper, green and brown butcher papers, glue, markers, index cards, colored chalk, and various art supplies to add special effects

Discovery Procedure

Cover the bottom third of a large board, wall or bulletin board with a strip of dark brown or black butcher paper approximately 12–18 inches in width, and label it *Floor*.

Cover the middle third of the board with light brown butcher paper or recycled brown grocery bags approximately 12–18 inches in width, and label it *Understory*.

Cover the top third of the wall with green butcher paper about 12–15 inches wide, and label it *Canopy*.

Plastic wrap can also be added to sections of the background to give a rain or waterfall appearance.

Students will then need to look at picture books and read about the rainforest layers to see what belongs in each layer. As students discover facts about the rainforest's plants and animals, have them draw their own pictures. Teachers can also help students or groups enlarge plant and animal pictures on an overhead or opaque projector.

Add three–dimensional vines by twisting brown and green paper into thin strips. For tree trunks, twist large sheets of brown butcher paper, brown sacks or combine several smaller twisted vines together. Students or groups can then staple plants and animals in the appropriate layer of the rain forest.

For example, a monkey would live in the canopy while a tarantula would live on the forest floor. Insects would appear not only on the forest floor, but also on the trunks of the trees in the understory.

Provide each student with index cards so they can write three or four descriptive sentences or words about their discoveries. Staple these cards next to the identified species. You may ask younger children to draw pictures or verbally communicate their findings.

Concept Development

✪What three layers of the forest did we study?
✪Do you think the layering system varies in rainforests in different parts of the world?
✪Do you think the layers are as distinct as we made them appear?
✪Where do you think the term tropical rainforest came from?
✪Is a jungle like a rainforest?
✪Why do you think the rainforests are disappearing or being destroyed? (Discuss in groups and report back to teacher and class).
✪Once destroyed, how easy do you think it is to replace the forest? Is it even possible?

Facilitator Facts

The three main layers of the rainforest are the floor, understory, and canopy. Towering above all the other plants in the forest are the giant trees called emergents. There are usually only one or two of these jungle giants per acre. Trees, shrubs, vines, ferns, and other plants that grow in the rainforest form a complex system of layers. The layering system varies from area to area, and the boundaries between the layers are often not distinct.

Tropical rainforests got their name because they are located in the regions between the Tropic of Cancer and the Tropic of Capricorn. By definition, rainforests get more than 60 inches of rain a year; some get 200–400 inches! The temperatures in a rainforest range from between 70° and 90°Fahrenheit.

People first used the word *jungle* to describe tropical forests when they traveled inland by boat to explore. These early explorers mistakenly assumed that the interior of the rainforest was like its overgrowing edges. However, inside the forest lies a magical, mysterious ecosystem.

Rainforest destruction (deforestation) is the result of a combination of environmental, social, political, and economical problems. Some common causes are:
- cattle ranching
- new settlers
- need for cash crops
- logging operations
- product demands
- construction of dams, roads, and other large–scale projects
- overpopulation

✪How many of these did your groups discuss?

When rainforests are destroyed, so are the habitats of many living things. Particularly at risk are rare species – plants or animals that are found only in one area. Destroying the habitats of rare species could easily result in their extinction.

140

Many items used daily in peoples lives come from the rainforest.
✪How do you think the destruction of the rainforests affects you?

Have students take *Forest Finders* (Worksheet 1) home. They are to check off the listed items which they find in their houses. (Discuss)
✪Which of those items are you willing to give up?
✪Were you surprised at how many rainforest products touch your daily life and household?

Encourage students to discuss the concept that not only does the destruction of the rainforest affect the plants and animals of that forest environment, but also the lives of people thousands of miles away.

Another expansion or group activity would be to remove and shuffle the index cards from the student created forest. Hand the cards back to students at random and ask them to correctly replace the cards in the forest. Continue to repeat this process in a game–like setting until students become confortable and confident in recognizing and labeling their rainforest discoveries.

Curriculum Connectors

Language Arts

This subject was previously integrated in the discovery stage when students were instructed to read rainforest literature and other resources in order to create the three–dimensional classroom bulletin board model.

Math

Sum Forest:
Inform students of the following rainforest facts. These facts can later be used for the basis of trivia questions, or can form the basis of student story problems. (Example: If it rains almost 200 days a year in the rainforest, how many days are without rain? 365 – 200=165)

•Scientists estimate that a rainforest area the size of a football field is destroyed each second.

•Tropical rainforests have from 80 to 240 inches of rain a year. It usually rains more than 200 days a year.

•About 3,000 rainforest plants can be used to make medicines that fight cancer.

•A few acres of rainforest in the Amazon basin have more species of plants than in all of Europe.

Sum Forest Facts
•An estimated 50 species of plants and animals becomes extinct every day in the world's rainforests.

•Rainforests grow in more than 50 countries but most are found in Brazil, Indonesia, and Zaire.

•In a Central American rainforest, you could find 950 different kinds of beetles on just one large tree.

•Rainforests are being cut down at a rate of 100 acres per minute.

•In the 1700s, 20 percent of Earth's land mass was covered with rainforests. In 1994, only 3–7 percent of the land is covered by rainforests.

Social Studies

Have students use a wall map, globe, textbook atlas or *Find–A–Forest* (Worksheet 2) to identify and label some countries or areas in which the tropical rainforests are found.

Have students map the route they would take to reach the rainforest closest to their own geographical area.

Younger students should simply see if they can locate the Tropic of Cancer, the Equator, and the Tropic of Capricorn on their classroom map or globe. Engage them in a discussion of why these areas are referred to as tropical.

Inform students that one great ancient civilization of the New World, the Maya, flourished for more than 600 years in the rainforests of Mexico and Central America. This richly complex society produced a wealth of cultural accomplishments:
•a 365–day calendar
•a written language
•expertly engineered and carved temples
•The mathmatical concept of zero

Today, many modern descendents of the Mayans still live in Central American rainforests. Also living in the same tropical forests are other Indian peoples like the Mbuti pygmies, the Lua, and the Penan. In addition, tucked away in ever shrinking pockets of the jungle are the remains of Stone Age

Health/Medicine

Over one–quarter of all medicines used in America are derived from rainforest plants. Along with the 3,000 other rainforest plants used to fight cancer, the Posy Periwinkle contains substances that have been used specificallyto treat Hodgkin's disease and leukemia. Of all the plants identified as having anticancer properties, 70 percent grow in the rain-forests. Many medicines are still in experimental and discovery stages.

Debate

Divide the class into Group One and Group Two. Group One wants to save the forest, and Group Two wants to cut it down to develop new industry and farming. Allow each group time to cooperatively discuss the pros and cons of their respective positions. Then, let the debate begin.

Trade Books

Animals in Danger: Forests of Africa - Gould
The Great Kapok - Cherry
The Rainforest Children - Pittaway
Where the Forest Meets the Sea - Baker
Wonders of the Rainforest - Crag
The Lorax - Seuss

Assessment Tips

Have students draw and label the three main parts of the rainforest. Make sure students list or draw some types of animals and plants that would be found in each layer.

Teacher observation and student involvement can assess this activity. The success of this activity will be evident if students demonstrate improved awareness of and stewardship toward not only the rainforests but also the environment closer to home.

Piggy Back Poem

It's Not Just a Jungle

Deforestation – what a ghastly word,
And a frightful situation.
Worst of all is the simple fact,
It's our very own creation!

Destroying the rainforest's layers,
The canopy, understory, and floor,
Is being done by farming and logging,
Industry, building, and more.

Preserving the balance of nature,
Should always be our goal,
Gently extracting the things we need,
Without taking an unhealthy toll.

Within the forest's complex system,
A variety of animals thrive.
From special plants that grow there,
Come medicines which help us survive.

For the things the rainforest gives us,
The spices, the oils, the wood.
For vegetables, fruits, and fibers,
Preservation – it's for our own good!

See if you can find some of these rainforest products in your home. Check (✔) the ones you find.

Forest Finders

FOODS

___avocado
___banana
___grapefruit
___lemon
___lime
___orange
___pineapple
___potato
___sweet potato
___tangerine
___tomato
___yam
___cashew nuts
___coconut
___coffee
___cola
___peanuts
___sugar
___tea
___rice

SPICES

___black pepper
___red pepper
___chili pepper
___chocolate
___cocoa
___cinnamon
___ginger
___mace
___nutmeg
___vanilla

MISCELLANEOUS ITEMS

___African violet plant
___insect repellent
___cocoa skin lotion
___cocoa soap
___printing ink
___rubber
___balloons
___erasers
___rubber balls
___rubber gloves
___rubber bands
___mahogany wood
___automobile tires
___wicker furniture

Can you find other items in your home made of rubber, wood, or substances that may have come from the rainforest? List them.

_____

_____

_____

_____

_____

Find–A–Forest

RAINFOREST AREAS

EQUATOR

TROPIC OF CANCER

TROPIC OF CAPRICORN

LABEL:

• North America, South America, Australia, Europe, Asia and Africa

• Atlantic, Pacific and Indian Oceans

LOCATE AND DRAW EACH OF THESE RAINFOREST COUNTRIES:

Costa Rica	Nigeria
Columbia	Congo
Zaire	India
Panama	Indonesia
Ecuador	Madagascar
Thailand	New Guinea

Crisco® Creatures

Wonder Wise

Have you ever **wondered why** penguins and other Arctic animals can stay warm in their frigid environments?

Concepts

Cold–weather animals, winter, harsh climate, Antarctica, penguins, seals, body heat, and insulation

Materials

Two large bowls, ice or snow, large and small plastic bags, solid Crisco® cooking shortening, and a thermometer

Discovery Procedure

Fill two large bowls half–full of ice cubes or snow. Put two or three cups of cooking shortening in a thick, large plastic bag; SEAL IT WELL. Flatten this bag and place on the ice in one bowl.

Have students test the temperature of the two bowls by placing one of their hands in the ice/snow bowl, and the other hand in the bowl of Crisco® covered ice/snow. (This is a particularly fun activity done in connection with the first snow of the season.) Students can also put their hands *inside* plain baggies and then into the Crisco® filled bags to test the ice temperature. It is messy, but fun!

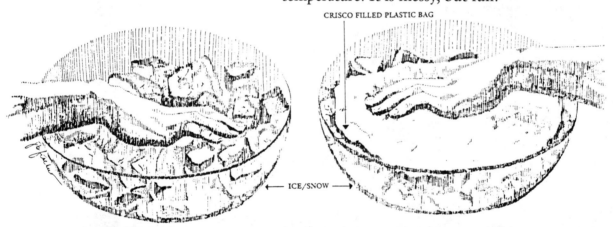

CRISCO FILLED PLASTIC BAG

← ICE/SNOW →

Concept Development

Discuss the difference in temperature between the two bowls. The bowl without the fatty protective layer will feel cold immediately. The other bowl of ice should not feel cold.
✪How do you think this experiment demonstrates an Arctic animals' ability to stay warm?
✪What do you think cooking shortening is made from? (animal or vegetable fat; have students read the shortening labels)
✪Do all penguins have short, compact bodies?
✪Do they have feathers or fur? (feathers)
✪How do you think they conserve body heat?

Penguins and other animals living in frigid locations keep warm with a layer of fat which is a form of body insulation. Their thick, oily coats provide a waterproof layer which helps them stay warm in extreme temperatures; 32° Fahrenheit to –129° Fahrenheit.

In addition to this insulating layer, animals like penguins find warm water holes and also huddle together in groups called rookeries, which further enable them to retain their body warmth. Rookeries can consist of more than 10,000 birds. Most animals, including humans, need a layer of fat to maintain body temperature.

Expansion

Have students place a thermometer in the ice cube bowl and another on top of the Crisco bag. They should take readings and record data from these thermometers at timed intervals. Classroom discussions concerning their findings should follow. This activity also serves as a math connection.

Curriculum Connectors

Language Arts

Have students tell or write a story about a penguin who wondered if he had knees; and if he does have knees, why does he walk the way he does?

Social Studies

Have the class locate the areas south of the equator where penguins and seals can be found. They live along the coasts of South America, South Africa, South Australia, New Zealand, and Antarctica.

Explain that Antarctica is the coldest place on Earth (45°– 74° below zero Celsius). Antarctica changes its size dramatically because of increasing and decreasing ice in the surrounding sea. It is the fifth largest

Art

Discuss, make or draw a penguin or seal in its proper environmental setting. Students may need to see pictures to help them.

P.E. Games/Role Play

There are many different *species* of penguins in the penguin *genus* (family). Have students act out these different species of penguins:

- Emperor Penguin - strut from side to side; waddle
- Chinstrap Penguin - nod the chin; nod, nod, nod
- Rocken Hopper - rock from side to side
- King Penguin - walk tall; walk, walk, walk
- Adelle Penguin - slide on your stomach; slide, slide

The class may want to find pictures in reference books of these and other types of penguins.

Assessment Tips

Have students write a brief statement about how penguins and other Arctic animals are adaptable to their environment. Answers could include: swim in warm water; short compact bodies; thick, oily outercoats; layer of insulating fat/blubber below the skin; and gathering/huddling in rookeries for warmth.

Trade Books

Mr. Popper's Penguins - Atwater
A Penguin Year - Bonners
Antarctica - Cowcher
Little Penguin - Bensen
Animals Should Definitely not Wear Clothing - Barrett

Piggy Back Poem

Pudgy Penguins

Said portly Peabody Penguin
To his wife, Priscilla Pat,
"You'd be so much warmer, dear,
If you'd just put on some fat!"

"But Peabody, how about this?"
Said Priscilla to her hubby.
"I'll just buy a new fur coat,
Instead of getting so chubby!"

148

Wonder Wise – A Vision Beyond Words

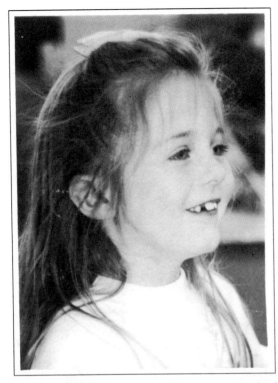

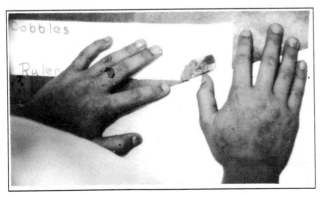

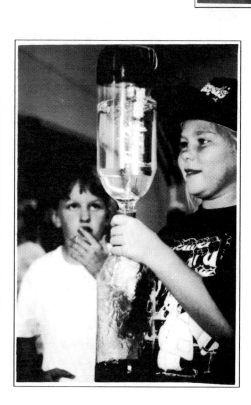

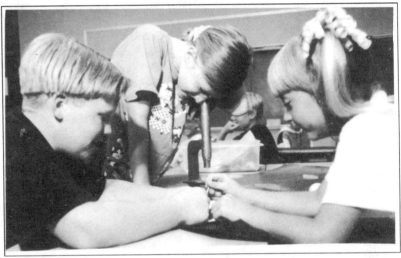

Assessment

Assessment Explanation

Assessment is of no use if it does not measure the things we value. The goals and objectives for learning must seek and focus on understanding and application to real–life problem solving. The task of assessment must be to make the *meaningful* measurable, not the *measurable* meaningful.

Observation is one of the most successful, yet most overlooked methods for assessing student understanding. Psychologists from Itard to Piaget to the present have watched children and adults perform to find their levels of understanding and developmental stages.

To adequately implement instruction in knowledge, skills, and attitudes in science, teachers should provide feedback from purposeful observations. Assessing hands–on activities should let students know that we value process with problem solving and communicating ideas to others. Traditional assessment that measures only the factual knowledge of students tells the students that the facts of science are all that we value. Good assessment must include process *and* content.

If we value science activities that engage students in multi–sensory experiences, then we must recognize the impact of student thinking and problem–solving during those experiences. Assessment must include teacher observation and recognition of student ideas.

Learning progresses at different rates for different students. Assessment must be on–going if we want to know how our students are developing concepts and internalizing knowledge. Assessment must be as flexible and as individual as our children. Knowledge, conceptual understanding, and internalization of that understanding take place all along the way. Conceptual understanding and real life connections provide the bridge to higher levels of cognitive development. Assessment must take place along the journey, not just at the end of the destination. It must be on–going to be meaningful.

Wonder Wise integrated science learning cycles advocate assessments that:
- assess what you want children to know and to do.
- are embedded within instructional materials.
- use a variety of methods to assess progress.
- emphasize teacher observation and inquiry questioning, and provide methods for getting to the perception behind individual answers.

Some of the types of assessment that provide for those goals are:
- teacher observations and checklists
- reading of student journals
- portfolios of student work
- performance assessments (indistinguishable from learning activities)
- interview and conferencing with students

The following page provides a suggestion for numerical ranking of teacher observations, interviews, etc. of individual students or small groups. These rankings can be used to help teachers construct scoring guidelines (rubrics) for various activities. Teachers must decide what children should know and be able to do as an indicator of their understanding about a given concept or set of related concepts. This tool encourages a less intimidating numerical ranking (1–5), but is easily adapted to other more traditional assessments.

Assessing Levels of Understanding

This number ranking is recommended to assist students and teachers in assessment of positive individual achievements.

5 | solid understanding on all concepts, able to extend and apply to other situations, phenomena

4 | solid understanding on major concepts, but still working on application, extension of concepts

3 | mixed understanding in major concepts

2 | little or poor understanding on most concepts and ideas

1 | little or no understanding, frustrated with concepts and ideas at this time

Assessment Checklist for Process Learning

This table is designed for quick, easy assessment at a glance, recognizing that many concepts children acquire through hands–on discovery learning cannot be evaluated in standardized forms.

Rank use of skills 1–5 (1 is lowest, 5 is highest).

observing, classifying, comparing, sorting (animals, rocks, plants, etc.)				
use of numbers, measures, shapes, patterns, and sequences				
interprets data, explains, organizes, and records collected data				
communicates results orally, composes graphs, charts, and pictorial labeling				
predicts, infers, questions, and explains possible outcomes based on observations				
manipulates, observes, replicates and builds models (ex. solar system)				
applies concepts in other situations				
makes decisions based on observations and collected information				
controls variables, recognizing the main factors that affect outcomes				
analyzes problems, hypothesizes, then tests				
uses tools of science (ex. thermometers, measuring tools, lenses				
organizes work areas and works cooperatively in large and small groups				
makes wise safety decisions				

This assessment checklist can be used as part of a quarterly report or individual activity reports, can be included in a portfolio or may be used as a tracking/pacing tool for classroom activities.

Assessment Form

Use this form as a quick checklist when making observations of students during *Wonder Wise* activities. All skills will not be utilized in all activities.

Student Name	Observe	Classify	Communicate	Record Data	Organize Data	Interpret Data	Infer and Predict	Use Numbers/Measures	Replicate Procedures	Make Decisions	Control Variables	Formulate Hypotheses
Squeezable Squid												
Spinnards												
Walking Water												
Color Mystery												
Skittle® Scatters												
Baffled By Bubbles												
Solids, Liquids, Gases & In Between												
Paper Path To The Moon												
DOC To The Moon												
Body Shadows												
Radical Rotations												
Rock & Mineral Candy Comparison												
Retrieving Rocks												
Cookie Expedition												
Cracker Quakes												
Rain, Rain, Come Again Another Day												
Recycled Big Books												
Pumpkin Probing												
Seedy Sidewalks												
Tators Are Tubers												
Germ Raiders & Tators												
Odor Decoder												
Worm Wonderment												
Recycled Rainforest												
Crisco® Creatures												

Assessment Form

Use this form as a quick checklist when observing students during hands–on activities. All skills will not be utilized in all activities.

Student Name

Activity Title/Description

	Observe	Classify	Communicate	Record Data	Organize Data	Interpret Data	Infer and Predict	Use Numbers/Measures	Replicate Procedures	Make Decisions	Control Variables	Formulate Hypotheses

Meet the Author

Karen Cornelsen Heizer brings a variety of experiences to *Wonder Wise*. She has taught elementary school in Oklahoma since 1980, served as a consultant for textbook companies, and presented workshops at State, National, and International NSTA Conferences.

Her numerous awards include the Presidential Award for Excellence in Science and Mathematics Teaching, the Christa McAuliffe Fellowship, and a Readers Digest National Award for Drug Education. Karen firmly believes in student centered learning. That belief is evident in both her teaching and her writing.

Karen lives in Enid, Oklahoma with her husband and two children.